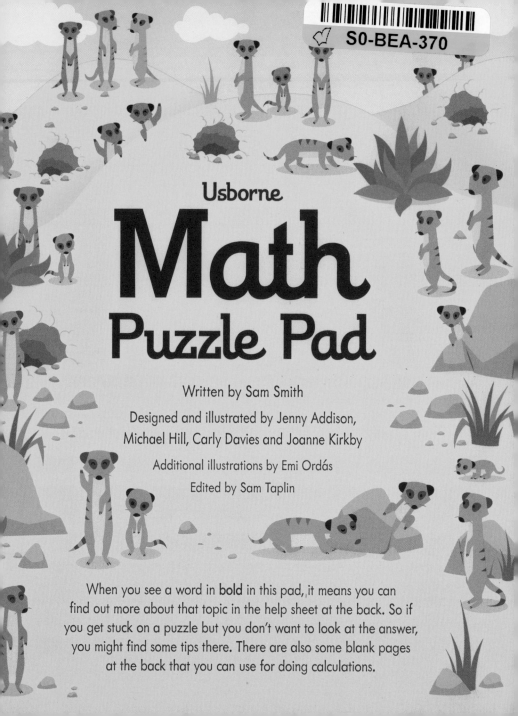

Usborne

Math
Puzzle Pad

Written by Sam Smith

Designed and illustrated by Jenny Addison,
Michael Hill, Carly Davies and Joanne Kirkby

Additional illustrations by Emi Ordás

Edited by Sam Taplin

When you see a word in **bold** in this pad, it means you can
find out more about that topic in the help sheet at the back. So if
you get stuck on a puzzle but you don't want to look at the answer,
you might find some tips there. There are also some blank pages
at the back that you can use for doing calculations.

Racetrack

The record lap time for this track is 2 minutes and 30 seconds. Add up the times on the flags. Has the racer below beaten the record lap time? Circle your answer on the sign at the bottom.

23s 5s 37s 4s 18s 4s 7s 12s 9s 9s 2

Yes / No

Farm fours

Write the numbers 1, 2, 3 or 4 in the empty squares without repeating a number in any row or column. The numbers in each outlined set of squares should add up to the small number in the corner of the set.

Number cruncher

What will happen to the number on each box as it goes through the machine? Write the new numbers on the matching boxes at the bottom.

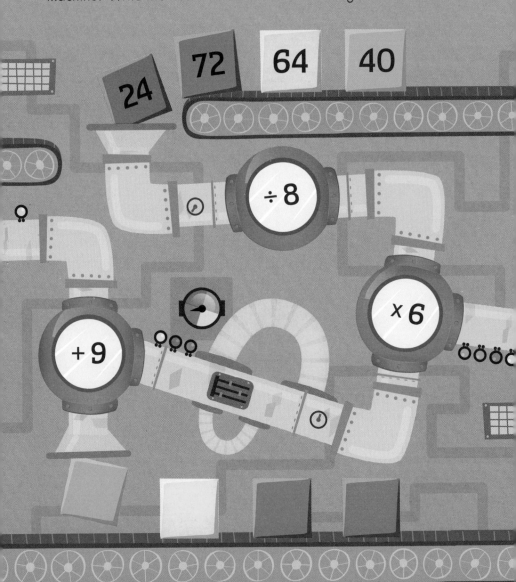

Pirate voyage

The *Black Dragon* is sailing to Treasure Cove, but there are obstacles along the way. Each obstacle will delay it for a certain amount of time. Use the key to add them all up, and find the quickest route.

23 minutes   14 minutes   19 minutes   29 minutes   *Black Dragon*

Treasure Cove

Across the ice

Help Suki cross the freezing water by drawing a line to mark her route. She can only step safely on ice-floe shapes that just have a single **line of symmetry.** Her first step has been shown for you.

Frog friends

Help Ferdie cross the pond to reach Filbert. He can only hop onto lily pads whose numbers can be divided by four.

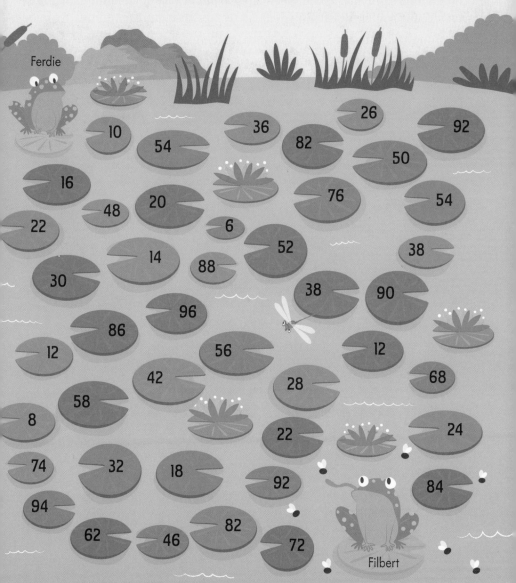

Chickens and eggs

Each of the chickens below laid four eggs. Some of the eggs have already hatched into chicks, but some of the unhatched eggs are missing. Draw the missing eggs onto the picture.

Number search

The answers to the calculations at the bottom of the page are hidden in the grid. They may be written in any direction. When you find each one, draw around it, as shown on the right.

1	2	7	3	6	0	4	7
9	8	0	3	6	4	9	6
7	4	2	4	0	5	3	8
2	9	5	9	8	6	0	7
9	5	3	3	2	4	8	5
8	0	8	2	0	7	4	9
5	3	1	7	4	8	2	0
6	3	1	0	7	3	1	4

$43+16+37 = ?$ $67+55+14 = ?$ $23×11 = ?$

$84÷6 = ?$ $174-117 = ?$ $95÷5 = ?$

$90×4 = ?$ $78÷3 = ?$ $108-31 = ?$

Toy store

Lizzie has 90 toy-store tokens to spend. If she only buys toys that cost an amount in the 4x table, circle the ones she chooses, then write how many tokens she has left.

Tokens left: . . . .

Delivering letters

Do the calculations on the envelopes at the bottom, then draw lines
linking each letter to the house whose number matches that answer.

| 0.5 x 10 | $\frac{2}{7}$ of 28 | 10% of 90 | $\frac{1}{9}$ of 63 | 84 ÷ 21 | 42.2 − 36.2 |

Destination data

The **pie chart** shows the types of trip 72 people like to take when they go away. How many people does each section represent? Use the angles to help you. (Remember that there are 360° in a circle.)

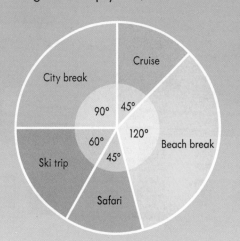

	Number of people
Ski trip:	
City break:	
Cruise:	
Beach break:	
Safari:	

Seaside scene

Multiply the number of crabs in this scene by the number of pieces of seaweed, then divide the answer by the number of flags. Add the result to the number of starfish. Write your answer on the sand castle below.

Kayak course

Circle the correct answers to the calculations on the board, then join up those numbers, from largest to smallest, to find the route the kayak will take around the obstacles.

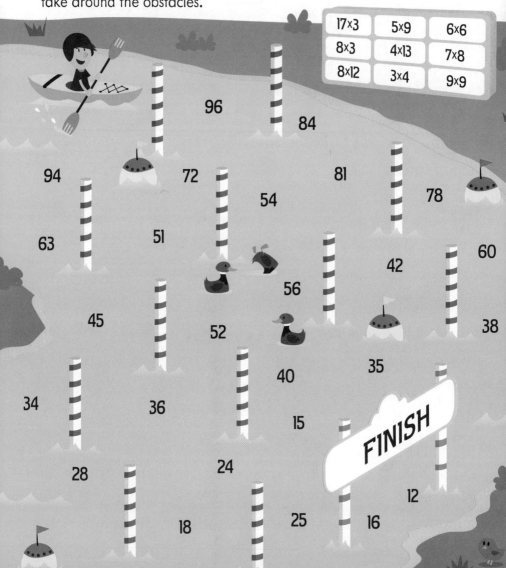

17×3	5×9	6×6
8×3	4×13	7×8
8×12	3×4	9×9

96

84

94

72

81

54

78

63

51

42

60

45

56

52

38

34

36

40

35

15

FINISH

28

24

12

18

25

16

Gymnastics

At an international gymnastics competition, a coach is making a note of how many medals each country wins, and in which age groups. Can you finish the chart by filling in the missing numbers?

	Under 12	Under 16	Total
America	4		14
Russia	8	9	
China			22
Great Britain	1		5
Total	22		

Planet problems

Do the calculations, then draw around the odd one out on each planet.

61 – 39
5.5 × 4
17.3 + 5.7
110 ÷ 5

48 × 0.5
12.5 + 11.5
72 – 47
144 ÷ 6

108 ÷ 12
3.75 + 4.25
63 – 54
2.25 × 4

85 ÷ 5
4 × 4.5
11.25 + 6.75
57 – 39

Dice spots

Draw the correct number of spots on the blank dice to complete all
of the calculations below.

1.

2.

3.

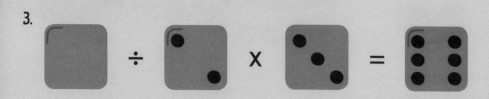

4.

Burger bar

How many cheeseburgers can be made from the ingredients below?
Each cheeseburger must be made following the recipe exactly.
Write your answer on the flag.

CHEESEBURGER RECIPE
(per serving)

1 burger bun
1 burger
3 slices of tomato

2 lettuce leaves
1 ring of onion
1 slice of cheese

2 packs of cheese slices
1 pack contains 10 slices

2 packs of burger buns
1 pack contains 6 buns

3 boxes of burgers
1 box contains 5 burgers

2 onions
1 onion gives 8 rings

4 tomatoes
1 tomato gives 6 slices

1 lettuce
1 lettuce gives 20 leaves

Fit all the numbers 1 to 9 into the grid below, so that the numbers in each row, column and diagonal line of three add up to 15. Three of the numbers have already been filled in for you.

Crazy golf

Do the calculations on the flags to find out Charlie's score on each hole. In golf, a low score is better than a high one. Did he beat the course record of 30?

1	2	3	4	5	6	7	Total
							. . . .
							Yes / N

25-23

1

$30 \div 10$

2

$1.5 + 2.5$

3

3×2

4

5

$49 \div 7$

$24 \div 6$

$52 - 47$

6

7

Robot workers

These robots have just come off the production line. The strongest is a builder, the fastest is a space explorer and the most intelligent is a doctor. Complete the calculations, then circle the robot that's a soldier.

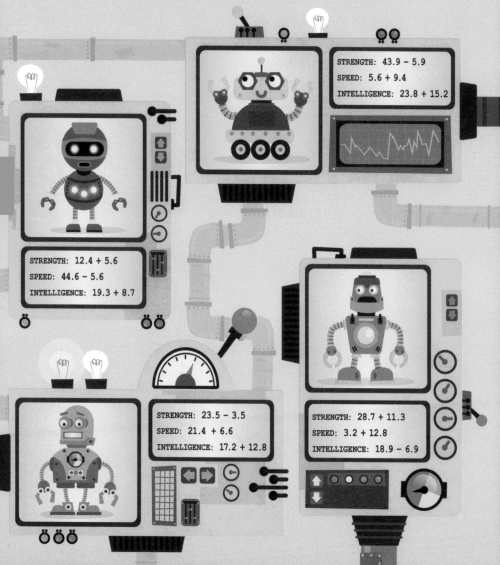

STRENGTH: 43.9 − 5.9
SPEED: 5.6 + 9.4
INTELLIGENCE: 23.8 + 15.2

STRENGTH: 12.4 + 5.6
SPEED: 44.6 − 5.6
INTELLIGENCE: 19.3 + 8.7

STRENGTH: 23.5 − 3.5
SPEED: 21.4 + 6.6
INTELLIGENCE: 17.2 + 12.8

STRENGTH: 28.7 + 11.3
SPEED: 3.2 + 12.8
INTELLIGENCE: 18.9 − 6.9

Which cube?

This pattern can be folded to make one of the cubes below. Can you figure out which one? Circle your answer.

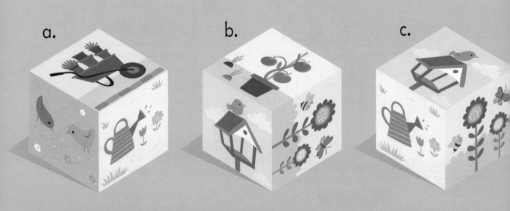

a.

b.

c.

Hidden picture

Fill in all the shapes that contain numbers that can be divided by six.
What can you see?

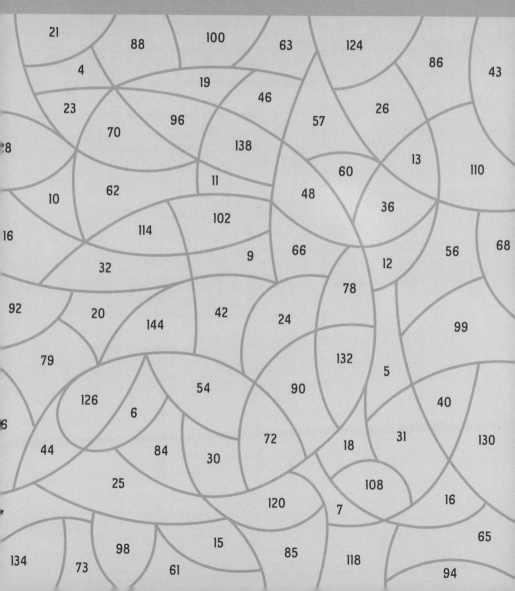

Cat calculation

What is the sum of the numbers that Tolly will go through on his way to his dinner?

Answer: . . . .

Building a nest

Birdie needs ten leaves to finish her nest, but can only use leaves with numbers that can be divided by twelve. Circle the leaves she can use. Will she have enough to finish it? Circle your answer on the nest.

132

108

11

60

130

100

72

78

105

82

43

108

74

36

68

98

84

Yes / No

96

24

116

94

48

144

66

34

126

In the jungle

25

Join all the dots in the order of the 2x table to reveal what is perching on this branch in the heart of the jungle.

Fish patterns

Give 40% of these fish stripes, then draw spots on a third of the unstriped fish. Give swirls to two fifths of the remaining fish. Finally, draw zigzags on half of the fish without stripes, spots or swirls. How many are left plain? Write your answer on the pink coral.

Butterfly farm

At the beginning of the month, there were 190 caterpillars at Budly Bloom Butterfly Farm. 30 were striped, 64 were spotted and 96 were hairy. By the end of the month, 12 of the striped caterpillars, 16 spotted ones and 72 hairy ones had transformed into butterflies. What **percentage** of each type of caterpillar had transformed?

Striped: ....

Spotted: ....

Hairy: ....

Domino sequences (28)

For each sequence, choose the domino at the bottom that completes it, and draw the correct number of dots on the double-blank domino.

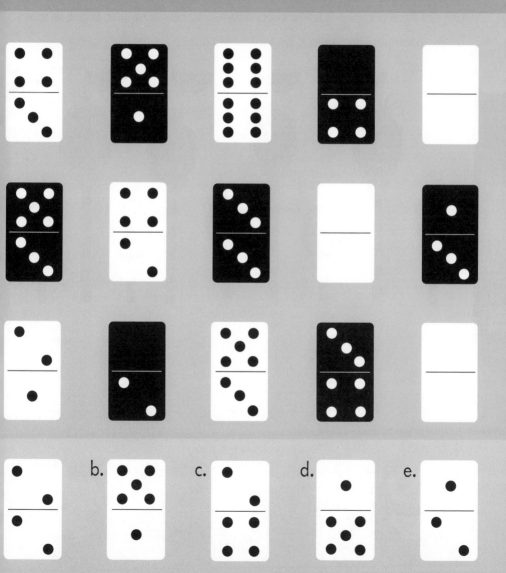

Coconut shy

This coconut shy gives out prizes for certain scores. If you want to win all the prizes below with nine throws, which coconuts must you hit to win each prize? Once a coconut is knocked down, you can't use it in another score. Draw three lines from each prize, to match it to the correct coconuts.

Starfish split

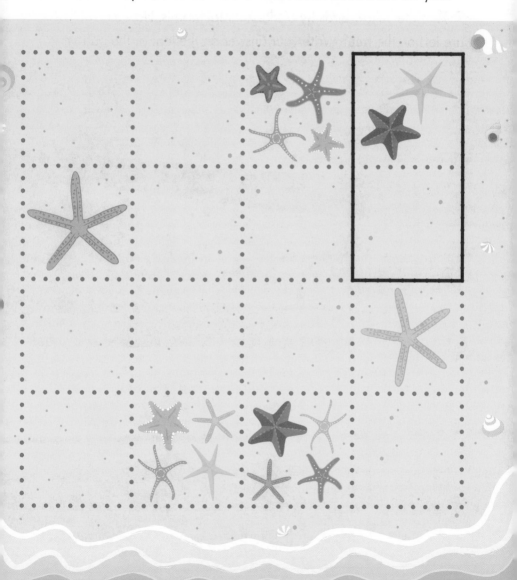

Draw lines to divide the grid into six areas. Each area must contain the same number of squares as starfish. One area has been done for you.

Birds on branches

Half the blue birds on this tree fly away to a tree with more shelter. Then all but two of the orange birds are scared off by a barking dog. 75% of the yellow birds fly off looking for worms. How many birds are left on the tree? Write your answer on the leaf at the bottom.

Canyon crossing

Ernest the explorer can only jump onto a stone column if the answer to its calculation can be divided by three. Which route must he take to reach the far side and explore the Lost Temple?

+13 64–31 82÷2 32÷4 24+68 72÷9 32+23

63–46 72÷3 70–31 75÷5 15+18 7×5

÷6 39+22 56÷8 2×22 39÷3 12÷4

12÷3 57–32 64÷4 56–19 32+15 23+55

–32 27÷9 47+27 98–23 44+28 99–42

72÷8 33+44 63–9 2×13 39+23 23+24

–23 52+42 84÷4 92–55 70–13 2×4

Ernest

Locomotive loads

These trains will leave the station in order, from heaviest to lightest. Fill in the blanks in each sequence, then write the sum of the four numbers on the locomotive to see how many units it weighs. Which train will leave first?

8   16   20

12   14

10   20

9   18

Top dogs

Fido, Benji and Rusty were the stars of the dog show. Rusty won by one point, but who scored what in each category? Finish filling in the table using the information below.

- There were two perfect scores of ten.
- Benji came first in tricks, and third in discipline.
- Fido came second in discipline and in appearance.

Dog's name	Discipline	Tricks	Appearance	Total
	8		7	20
	6		8	
			6	

Fastest route

James is going to the park, but his dad needs him to go to the supermarket and bakery on his way. Add up the times on each road to find the fastest route from home to the stores, to the park and back home. He can't retrace any of his route along the main roads, or visit the castle more than once.

Darts scores

In this special game of darts, you have to throw three darts into the dartboard and can only hit each section once. The inner sections on this dartboard are double the value of the outer ones.

a. What's the lowest score you can make? ....

b. What's the highest score you can make? ....

c. How many different ways can you reach a target score of ten with three darts? ....

Bridge crossing

If you step on a plank with an incorrect calculation on it, you'll fall to your doom. Cross out the planks you should avoid to cross the bridge safely.

$42 \div 7 = 7$

$17 \times 4 = 68$

$96 - 58 = 38$

$13 + 29 = 44$

$62 \times 4 = 248$

$335 - 177 = 156$

$63 \div 7 = 9$

$14 \times 5 = 72$

Maze meeting

How long will Bill take to reach his friend Ben? Add up the number of seconds along his route, then write your answer in minutes.

Bill

Ben

Answer: . . . .

On the seabed

Join the groups of dots to finish this underwater picture. The blue dots follow the 7x table, and the purple dots follow the 9x table.

Taking taxis

The small taxis can carry four passengers and the big taxi can carry six.
Are there enough taxis for everyone? Circle your answer on the sign.

Cross-number

Use the clues at the bottom to put the correct numbers into the grid.

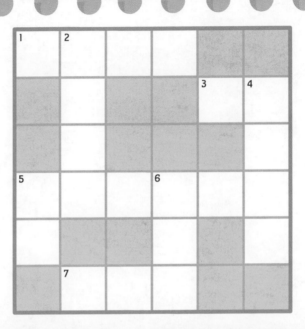

Across →

1. 1,089 + 1,268

3. 180 ÷ 4

5. One hundred and six thousand, nine hundred and eighty-three

7. 2,832 divided by the number of sides a square has

Down ↓

2. The number of degrees in a circle x the number of sides on two pentagons

4. 17,780 − 12,041

5. 137 − 72 − 49

6. 227 x 4

Balancing act

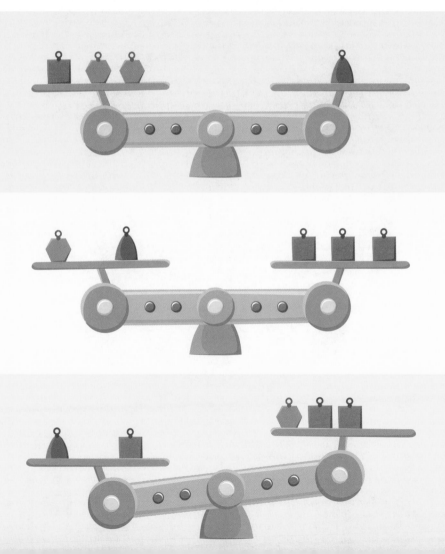

42

The first two sets of scales below are balanced, but the bottom set is not. Which weight should you add on the right-hand side to make the third set balance? Draw your answer on the scales.

Token total

You have a pocketful of tokens to spend at the fair. You use an eighth of them to buy ice cream. Then you spend seven to ride the roller coaster, but drop a quarter of your remaining tokens looping the loop. You now have 21 tokens – how many did you have to start with?

Answer: . . . .

House of horrors

All the prices in this store are in Horrors. How much change will you have from 50 Horrors (H50) if you buy everything on the list below?

H16

Monster Jokes

Frightfully funny
Part II

Frightfully funny
Part I

Frank N. Stein

H4

Shopping List

1 monster joke book

1 dozen eyeballs

2 bowls of worms

36 magic beans

1 pair plastic monster specs

2 jars pickled brains

Change: ....

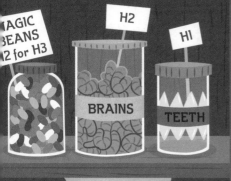

MAGIC BEANS
12 for H3

H2

H1

BRAINS

TEETH

H8

H8

H8

H10

H3 per bowl

4 for H1

H8

Nectar numbers

Each of these buzzing bees can only collect nectar from a flower with a number that can be divided by its own. Draw a circle around the bee that won't have any nectar to take back to the hive.

Cross sum

Fill in each blank square with a number from 1 to 9. The numbers in each row or column should add up to the total shown on the arrows. (The direction of the arrows shows you whether to add across or down the grid.) You can use numbers more than once, but only once in each answer. For example, you can make 4 with 3 and 1, but not with 2 and 2.

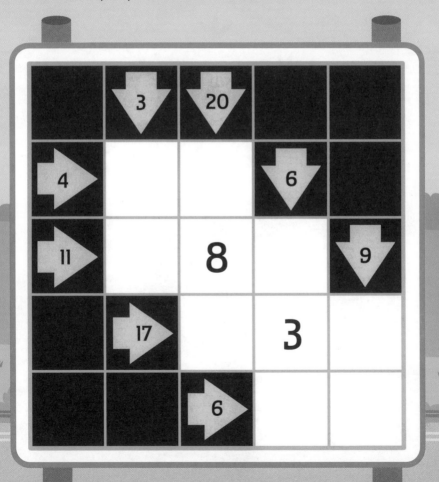

Seating arrangements

The Millers have bought tickets for The Talent Show. They'll all be sitting together, and their seat numbers add up to their joint age. Mrs. Miller is 33 years old and her husband is two years older. Their two twins are a fifth of their father's age. Circle which seats they'll sit in.

Cake decorating

Draw the finishing touches on the cupcakes below, using as many
decorations from the jars as possible to make them extra special.
All three cakes must have the same amount of each decoration,
though, so count carefully before you begin.

26 sprinkles

8 flakes

11 marshmallows

5 cherries

4 ribbons

Circles and squares

Fit all the numbers 1 to 9 into the grid, so the four squares around each circle add up to that circle's total, and the green, orange and red squares add up to the totals at the bottom. Two numbers have been filled in for you

Bubble burst

Only the bubbles with a number inside them that can be divided by seven will reach the surface. Cross out all the bubbles that will burst.

27 21 43 65 49

91 56 77 14 84

32 98 54

28 7 63 44

94 35

Coconut climb

Starting with the bottom number, do all the calculations up the trunk of each tree. The answer you're left with when you get to the top is how many rungs you can climb up that tree's ladder. Which bunch of coconuts can you reach?

Tree 1:
÷8
×4
+6
×7
2

Tree 2:
÷5
+19
−7
×6
8

Tree 3:
÷2
×4
−5
×3
4

Castle copy

Draw a new tower on the grid, exactly the same shape, but moved six squares to the right and four squares up.

This **pie chart** shows what 60 people like to do when they're at the park. How many people does each section represent? Use the angles to help you. (Remember that there are 360° in a circle.)

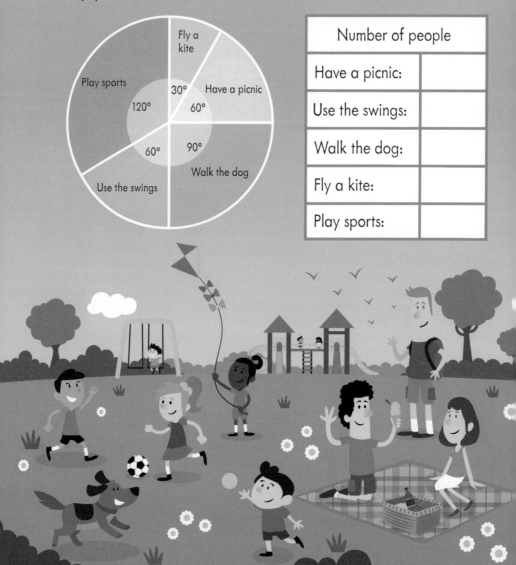

Number of people	
Have a picnic:	
Use the swings:	
Walk the dog:	
Fly a kite:	
Play sports:	

Birthday surprise

Join the dots following the order of the 4x table to see the delicious treat that's waiting to be eaten on the plate.

Bingo buddies

55

Haley and Josh are playing bingo. They cross out a calculation on their card when a ball is picked out that has its answer on it. Play the game using the balls below, and draw a star on the winner's card.

BINGO CARD - Haley

7×8	67+29	16×5	14+47
22×4	140÷5	118−54	105÷15

BINGO CARD - Josh

41+47	62−19	4×7	240÷3
12×6	207÷9	39+38	113−17

96   88   7   23   43   77   56   72   28   61   80

How many triangles can you find hidden in this pattern?

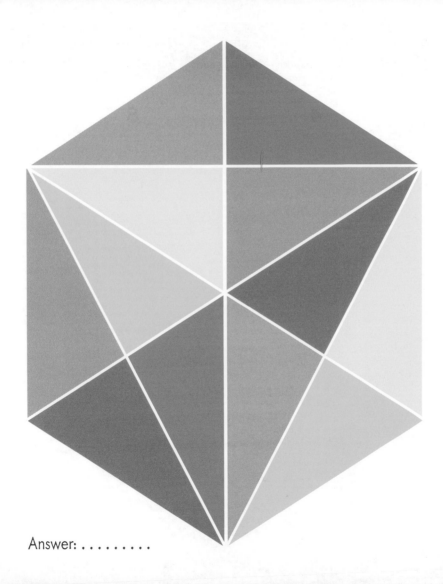

Answer: . . . .

Fruit filling

Finish filling in this table to show how many pallets, crates and boxes each type of fruit will fill, and how many pieces of fruit will be left unpacked.

Amount to be packed	Pallets (1,000 items each)	Crates (100 items each)	Boxes (10 items each)	Single items left unpacked
4,187 pineapples	4	1	8	7
58,713 apples				
74,607 oranges				
406,079 bananas				
2,309,218 strawberries				

Airport maze

Trace the route that the plane goes to the runway if it takes the way with the number that can be divided by three at each turn.

Crossing the lake

This family has to be rowed across to Granny's island by the boatman. His boat has three seats that can each hold a passenger or an item of luggage, but there must always be another adult in the boat. How many trips must he make there and back to take the family and luggage across?

Crossings today

. . . .

Flower show

Circle the flower arrangement that took the longest to create.

Started

Finished

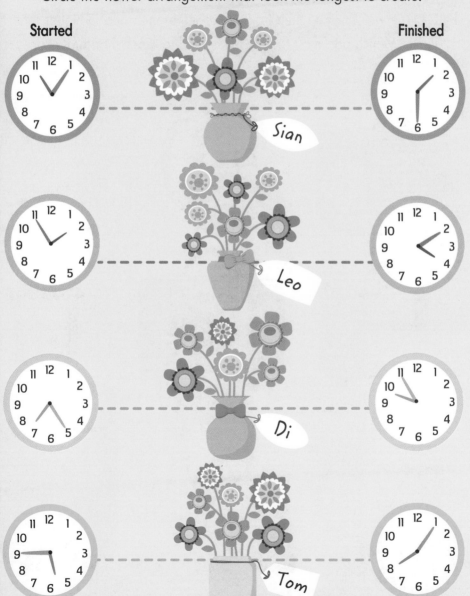

Sian

Leo

Di

Tom

A group of friends is going on a small plane, but their luggage is too heavy. The weight of all their luggage together must not be higher than 120 units. Which bag must they leave behind to reach that total exactly?

Shape fitting

All but one of the shapes below can fit together with themselves without leaving gaps in between, like the red T-shape. Try drawing each shape fitted together with itself on its grid, then circle the shape that can't do this.

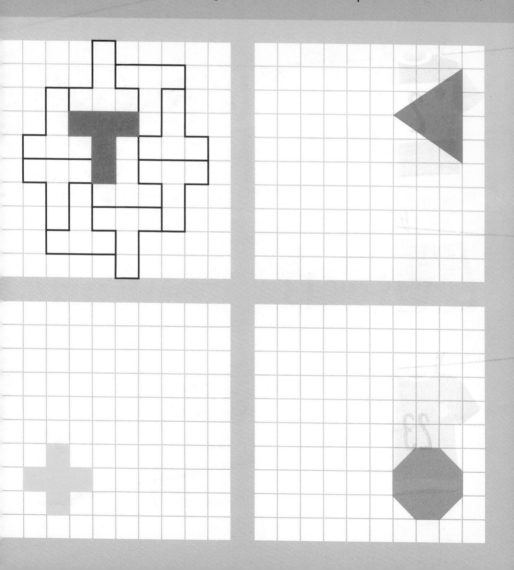

Washing lines

These sports clothes have been hung up to dry in ascending order. Fill in the missing **prime numbers** from the sequence, then circle the items that belong to Billy, whose clothes have numbers on them ending in nine.

Pool planner

The pool manager is making a chart to find out if children of different ages tend to use the pool at different times. Can you finish the chart by filling in the missing numbers?

	Morning	Afternoon	Total
2 – 4 years old	7		8
4 – 6 years old		2	13
6 – 8 years old	12	9	
8 – 10 years old			32
Total	36		

Which line of traffic will be the fastest through the tunnel and which will
be the slowest? Multiply the numbers of luggage items on all the vehicles
in each line together. The smaller the answer, the quicker the traffic.

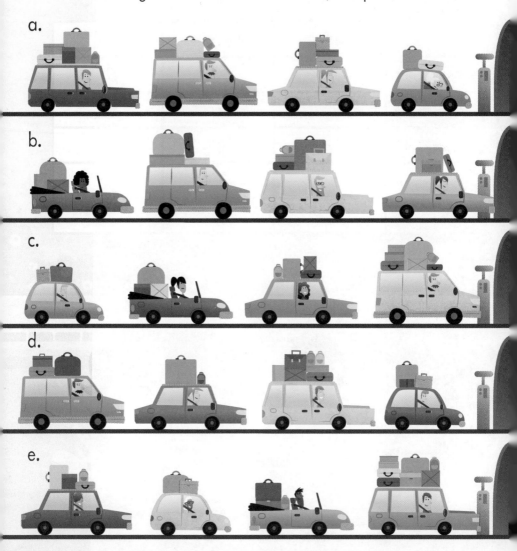

Ice skaters

Draw hats on 25% of the skaters, then draw scarves on a third of the skaters without a hat. Finally, draw earmuffs on two-thirds of the skaters who still aren't wearing a hat or a scarf. How many skaters aren't wearing any of these winter clothes now? Write your answer on the sign.

Pyramid puzzle

Some of the numbers are missing from this pyramid. Write the missing numbers on the blank stones. Each number is the sum of the two directly underneath it.

257

64

31

8   17   14

6   16   5

Airport luggage

Each of the luggage carts at this airport can hold seven items of luggage. Are there enough carts in the picture to hold all the items of luggage on the carousels?

Yes / No

Can you fit all seven shapes below inside the square without rotating them, and without any overlapping or going outside the lines? Draw the shapes in the correct positions in the square, or cut them out and arrange the pieces.

Hidden picture

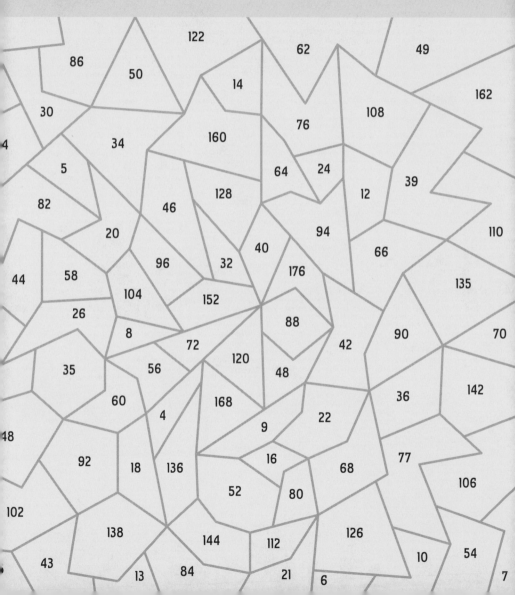

Fill in all the shapes that contain numbers that can be divided by eight.
What can you see?

Under the sea

These sea creatures stand for numbers. The fish is worth twice the value of the jellyfish, and the shark is worth twice the fish. Fill in the missing values.

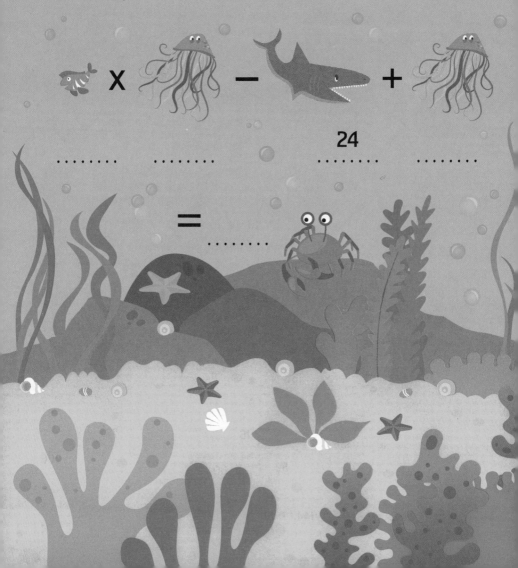

.... 24 ....

= ....

Sequence search

Draw lines through the numbers that follow the sequences described
below. The lines zigzag across either from left to right or right to left,
as shown in the example. Each sequence is five numbers long.

1. Count in 7s from 40.
2. Count in 6s from 41.
3. Count in 4s from 56.
4. Count in 3s from 7.
5. Count in 2s from 60.

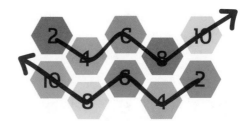

6   8   78   40   19

15   10   16   2   7   10

7   13   19   12   6

64   72   64   56   64   64

69   68   60   60   69

9   6   17   41   9   9

41   53   65   62   0

72   47   59   40   72   72

38   96   19   47   1

62   72   41   66   62   62

87   60   68   64   60

12   56   47   61   12   12

53   40   54   68   7

11   20   53   99   54   11

47   39   16   22   3

Number mix

Each purple potion number has been made by multiplying a red potion number by a yellow one. If each number has been used only once, draw lines between the pairs of potions that have been multiplied together, and circle the red and yellow potions that haven't been used.

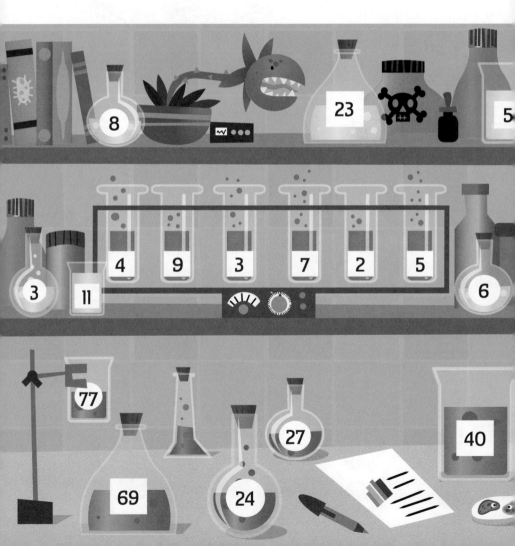

Whichever route Granny Douglas takes home, there are obstacles that add time to her journey. Which route is quickest?

25 seconds 10 seconds 45 seconds 60 seconds

There's a 20% discount on all items at the pirate emporium, but the price tags haven't been changed yet. How much change from 200 silver pieces will Redbeard receive if he buys all the items on his list below?

Shopping List

2 parrots
1 globe
12 gold goblets
1 captain's hat
5 hooks
15 bottles citrus juice

Change: ....

35 pieces

3 pieces

Citrus

Lime

12 pieces

5 pieces

30 pieces

7 pieces

3 pieces

10 pieces

4 pieces

How to be a pirate II

How to be a pirate I

Treasure
A beginner's guide

Minigolf

Add up the scores on this minigolf scorecard to find out who won.
Underline the winning player (the player with the lowest score).

MINI 9

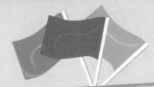

Scorecard

Hole name	Jamie	Sara	Zoe
1. Pirate Ship	4	3	4
2. Rabbit Warren	3	6	5
3. Dinosaur	5	7	8
4. Toadstool	9	4	7
5. Dungeon	8	5	6
6. Lighthouse	7	8	8
7. Anthill	6	4	5
8. Dracula's Castle	8	9	6
9. Windmill	7	10	9
TOTAL	....	....	....

Duck directions

Guide the duck through the maze back to her ducklings.
What is the sum of the numbers she swims across on her way?

Answer:
. . . .

Petal count

Suzie likes flowers with an even number of petals and Samir prefers flowers with an odd number of petals. Put a cross in the flower above the name of the person who will have the biggest bouquet.

Suzie   Samir

Six sudoku

The grid below is made up of six blocks, each containing six squares.
Fill in the blank squares so that each block, row and column contains
all the numbers 1 to 6.

...for the **coordinates** at the bottom on this chart, then join the...
...n order. What shape do they make? (The first number in eac...
...pair shows how many squares to count across from 0. The sec...
...shows how many to count up or down.)

(0, 4) (1, 1) (4, 1) (2, -1)
(3, -4) (0, -2) (-3, -4)
(-2, -1) (-4, 1) (-1, 1) (0, 4)

Bees and hives

All these bees live in the two hives below. If ten more bees live in the big hive than live in the small hive, write on each hive how many bees live in it.

Toolbox trouble

This builder has emptied his toolbox, looking for the tool he's missing.
He should have 7 wrenches, 16 bolts, 8 screwdrivers and 6 hammers.
Draw the missing tool.

Cross sum

Fill in each blank square with a number from 1 to 9. The numbers in
each row or column should add up to the total shown on the arrows.
(The direction of the arrows shows you whether to add across or down
the grid.) You can use numbers more than once, but only once in each
answer. For example, you can make 4 with 3 and 1, but not with 2 and 2.

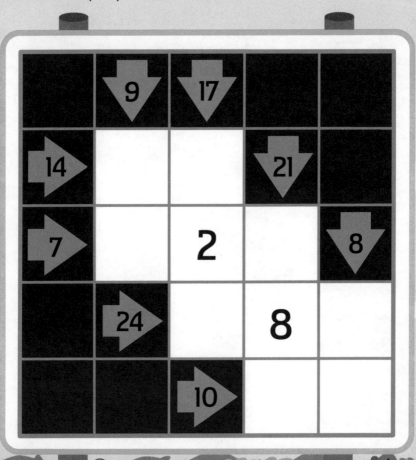

Strength test

Mia, Lewis and Sophie tested their strength on the machine below. Mia and Lewis went first and their scores flashed up on the machine. If Sophie's score was exactly halfway between Mia's and Lewis's, what did she score? Write your answer in the purple section below.

112

177

Which cube?

This pattern can be folded to make one of the cubes below. Can you figure out which one? Circle your answer.

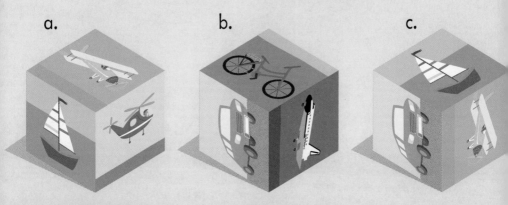

a.

b.

c.

Racing roller coasters

Figure out the sequence on each roller coaster and fill in the numbers on the blank cars. The fastest roller coaster is the one with the numbers that add up to the lowest total – circle it.

7 11 19 31

39 27 18 12

8 16 32 128

Hungry robot

This number-munching robot eats anything that can be divided by six or eight. Circle the numbers he eats.

24 13 78

62 58 43

20

16

31

5

54

42

37

15

36

2 72 27

33

96 64

Car categories

Four people have bought new cars. The banker's does the most miles to the gallon, the movie star's has the highest top speed, and the stunt driver's does 0-60 in the shortest time. Complete the calculations, then circle the car that belongs to the farmer.

0-60 time: 49−37
Top speed: 300÷3
Miles per gallon: 5x6

0-60 time: 28÷7
Top speed: 30x4
Miles per gallon: 12+11

0-60 time: 70÷10
Top speed: 12x11
Miles per gallon: 83−64

0-60 time: 200÷20
Top speed: 56+43
Miles per gallon: 77−48

Ski race

Add up the number of seconds on each set of flags and circle the skier who comes down the slope the quickest (the lowest total wins).

Planet puzzle

Write the numbers below on the red planets so that each side of the square adds up to 25 and all the numbers are used.

5   7   11   12

A pirate and his crew are sailing to the Isle of Skulls in search of its fabled hoards of gold. Follow the descriptions to discover which three directions the compass needle points to during the voyage. The needle starts at North (N).

Answers:

The needle swings 45° clockwise.	
Then, it swings 270° in the opposite direction.	
Lastly, it swings 135° clockwise.	

Roman emperors

This timeline shows the ruling dates for seven of the emperors of the Roman empire. Use it to find out the answers to the questions below.

Tiberius	Gaius	Claudius	Nero	AD 68 – AD 69 Civil War	Vespasian	Titus	Domitian
AD 14	AD 37	AD 41	AD 54	AD 68 AD 69		AD 79	AD 81	AD 96

1. Which emperor had the third longest reign?

....

2. Which emperor's reign was twice as long as the reign of one of the other emperors?

....

3. Mount Vesuvius erupted 42 years after Gaius's reign began. In which year was the eruption?

....

4. If Tiberius became emperor at the age of 55, how old was he when his rule ended?

....

Owl symmetry

Only half of the owl has been drawn on the grid below. Draw its **mirror image** on the right-hand side of the grid to complete the picture.

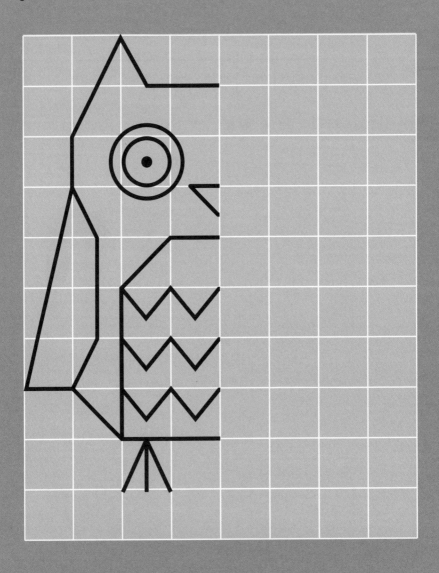

Picture code

Each picture below stands for a different number from 1 to 4. The numbers at the edges of the grid are the sum of the numbers in each row or column. Can you figure out which picture represents which number?

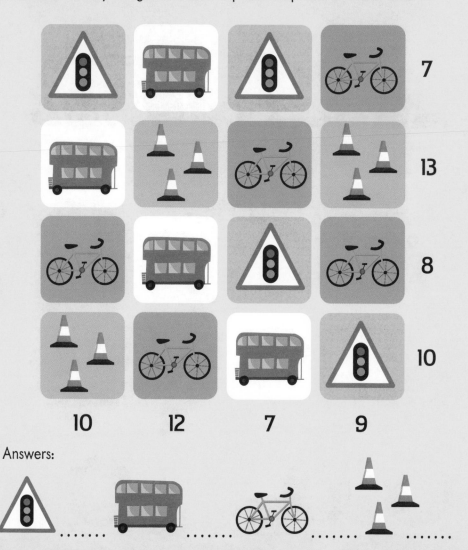

Answers:

Plane passengers

95

The shuttle bus below is full. If the plane is fully booked and holds 133 passengers, how many round trips will the shuttle bus need to make to take everyone to the aircraft? Write your answer on the door of the bus.

There's only time for three aliens to jump down each crater before the enemy spaceship lands. How many will be left out in the open? Write your answer on the top crater.

Apple picking

Add apples to the empty trees in the orchard so that the apples along each side of the triangle add up to 17. Each tree must have between 1 and 9 apples and no two trees can have the same amount of apples.

Pipes puzzle

Follow the calculations along the pipes, and write the answer to each stage in the round windows. What number will come out of the pipe? Write the final answer in the yellow box at the bottom of the page.

56

÷8 .... −3 ×9 ....

×2

×3 −11 +21 ÷9 ....

+17 −2 .... ÷3

+7

Beach fours

Write the numbers 1, 2, 3 or 4 in the empty squares without repeating a number in any row or column. The numbers in each outlined set of squares should add up to the small number in the corner of the set.

Sudoku

The grid is made up of nine blocks, each containing nine squares. Fill in the blank squares so that each block, row and column contains all the numbers 1 to 9.

		5	1			2		
7			9			5	8	
	1	9			4		3	7
5			7			4	6	2
		2				7		
1	7	6			8			9
3	2		8			1	4	
	6	1			5			3
		4			2	9		

Space race

The rocket is heading to the orange planet, but there are obstacles along the way, and each one will delay it by a certain amount of time. Use the key to add them all up and find the fastest flight path.

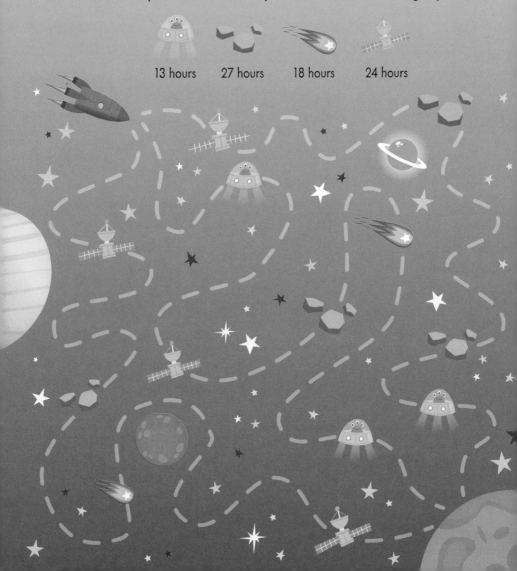

13 hours 27 hours 18 hours 24 hours

Rocket re-size

Draw a rocket on the grid, exactly the same shape as the orange one, but twice as big. The first part has been done for you.

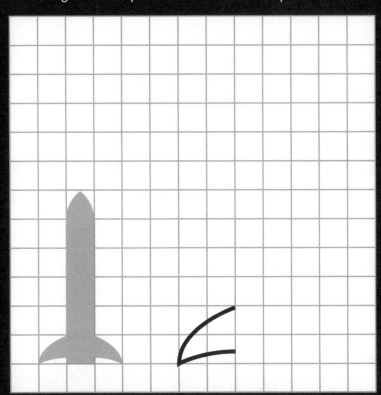

Hidden hieroglyphs

Figure out what the sequence is on this Egyptian snake charm, then draw on the symbols that are missing from the empty sections.

Picture code

Each picture below stands for a different number from 1 to 4. The numbers at the edges of the grid are the sum of the numbers in each row or column. Can you figure out which picture represents which number?

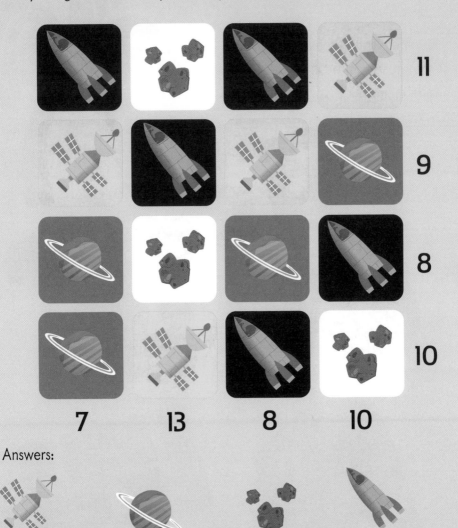

Answers:

....

Treasure chests

A chest only contains treasure if its number can be divided by...

... seven,

... or eight,

... or twelve.

Help the pirates by marking with an X the chests that have some treasure inside them.

Sailing fours

Write the numbers 1, 2, 3 or 4 in the empty squares without repeating
a number in any row or column. The numbers in each outlined set of
squares should add up to the small number in the corner of the set.

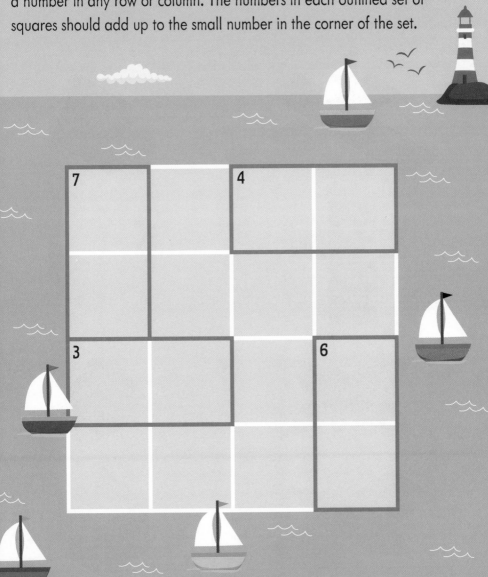

Folding shapes

The 2-D shapes on the left below can be folded to make the 3-D shapes on the right. Draw a line from each 2-D shape to the 3-D shape it can be folded into.

Town planning

Draw two overlapping ovals around the town below to group the buildings into three categories:

- in the first oval, buildings with a red front door
- in the second oval, buildings with more than three front windows
- in the overlap, buildings with a red front door and more than three front windows.

Safe cracker

You're a detective on the trail of an infamous jewel thief, and have just found his safe, along with the instructions at the bottom. Can you use them to crack the safe's combination and recover the lost gems? (Remember, every time you turn the dial, you will move a new number to the top. Start with 0 at the top of the dial.)

Answers:

Turn the dial 60% clockwise.	
Then, turn the dial 90% in the opposite direction.	
Then, turn the dial 25% clockwise.	
Lastly, turn the dial 85% in the opposite direction.	

Only half of the monster has been drawn on the grid below. Draw its **mirror image** on the left-hand side of the grid to complete the picture.

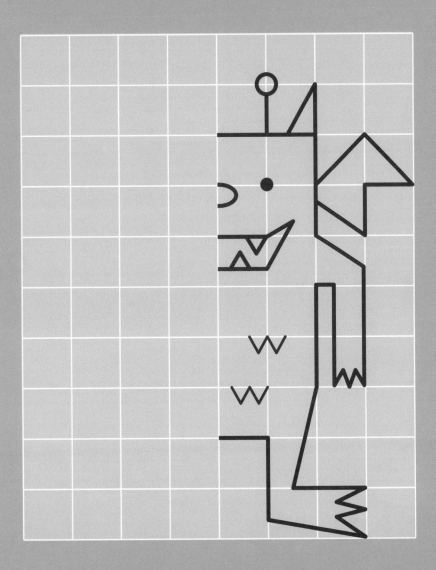

Pharaoh timeline

This timeline shows which pharaohs ruled Ancient Egypt between 1334 BC and 1213 BC. Use it to find out the answers to the questions below.

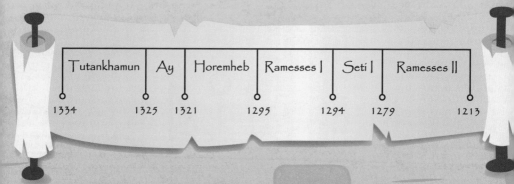

Tutankhamun	Ay	Horemheb	Ramesses I	Seti I	Ramesses II
1334	1325	1321	1295	1294	1279	1213

1. Underline the name of the pharaoh who had the longest reign.

2. Circle the name of the pharaoh who had the shortest reign.

3. How long was Horemheb's reign?

....

4. If Tutankhamun came to the throne at age nine, how old was he when his rule ended?

....

Turning tools

Circle the two sets of tools that can be rotated so that they match each other exactly.

a.

b.

c.

d.

e.

f.

Butterfly wings

Fill in the missing numbers so that multiplying the numbers on a butterfly's top wings gives the same answer as when you multiply those on its bottom wings. One has been done for you.

Out in space

The parts of this picture that are the same shade as each other contain numbers from the same times table. Figure out which times table goes with each shade, then write it in the matching star. The first one has been done for you.

Missing angles

Figure out the size of **angles** a, b, c and d in this picture, and write them at the bottom. Use these rules to help you:
• All the angles on a straight line add up to 180°.
• All the angles inside a triangle add up to 180°.
• All the angles inside a four-sided shape add up to 360°.

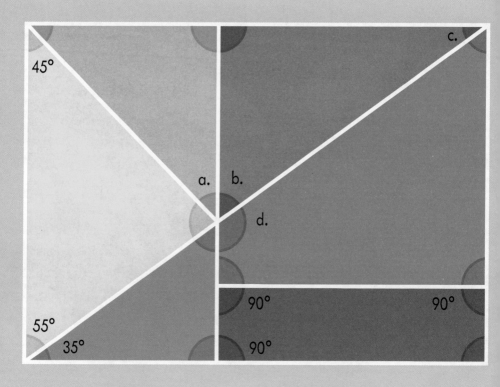

a. ....   b. ....   c. ....   d. ....

Germ colony

Each of these germs splits into two new germs every day, and the next day the new germs also split into two new germs. If today is Thursday, how many germs were there to begin with on Tuesday?

Answer: ....

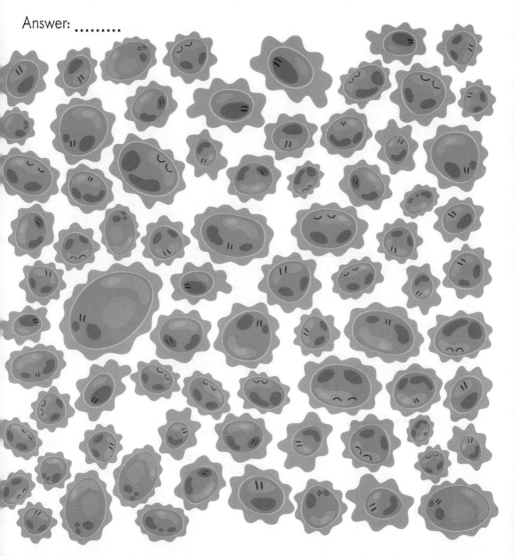

Street scene

In the picture below, the number of houses = H, the number of windows = W, the number of roofs = R, the number of chimneys = C, the number of pot plants = P and the number of doors = D.

Some of the calculations below are not correct. Read through them all carefully, and write "true" or "false" next to each one.

1. W – H = D + C	
2. P + R + H = W – C	
3. W ÷ R = P x P	
4. D + R = W ÷ P	
5. H + D = C x P	

Hidden picture

Fill in all the shapes that contain numbers that can be divided by three.
What can you see?

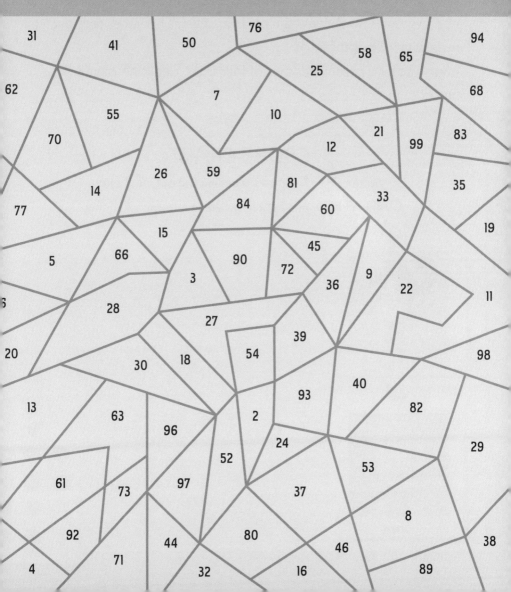

Sam and Lyla are given stickers for doing household chores. Draw the stickers onto the chore chart below to find out who gets the most if:

• Lyla vacuums twice, feeds the cat twice, cleans her room once and does laundry twice.
• Sam vacuums once, feeds the cat four times, cleans his room twice and does laundry once.

CHORE CHART

Vacuuming - 2 stickers Feeding the cat - 1 sticker
Cleaning bedroom - 1 sticker Doing laundry - 2 stickers

Lyla

Sam

Gone fishing

Each of these anglers only catch the fish that can be divided by the number in front of them. Circle all the fish that won't be caught.

Weight lifters

Multiply the numbers on each weight, then add the answers together to find out how much each man is lifting. Write each weight lifter's score on the card next to him, then circle the strongest man.

Circles and squares

122

Fit all the numbers 1 to 9 into the grid, so the four squares around each circle add up to that circle's total, and the purple, yellow and blue squares add up to the totals at the bottom. Two numbers have been filled in for you.

19   17

8   4

23   23

8   13   24

Which bus?

Use this timetable to answer the questions below.

Departures						
Ardbury	09:35	10:00	10:15	10:35	10:55	11:20
Fenton	09:55	10:20		10:55		11:40
Old Bar	10:30	10:55	11:10	11:30	11:50	12:15
Wellville	10:45	11:10		11:45	12:05	

Simon catches the 09:35 bus from Ardbury and stops off in Old Bar for an hour and fifteen minutes. What time is the next bus to Wellville that he can catch?

Answer:
....

Charlotte wants to spend at least an hour in Fenton, and then be in Old Bar by 12:20. What time is the latest bus she can catch from Ardbury?

Answer:
....

Cattle round-up

Ned Pepper is rounding up cattle. It takes him 1 minute and 30 seconds to round up each of the ones with horns, and 45 seconds to round up each of the ones without horns. How long does it take him to round up all the cattle outside the pen? Write your answer in Ned's lasso.

Cube in a cube

Only one of the little cubes at the bottom can fit into the space in the large cube to complete the pattern. Which one is it?

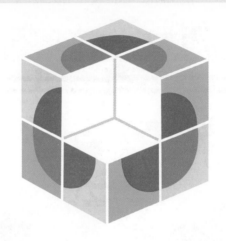

a.

b.

c.

d.

e.

f.

Snails and leaves

Sandy can only eat numbers that can be divided by 8 and Sidney can only eat numbers that can be divided by 12. Circle the leaves that will not be eaten by either snail.

Sandy

Sidney

14
48
28
18
92
36
39
32
84
42
8
24
62
88
45
12
72
80
54
51
34
40
16
96
74
78
60

Multiplying machine

Find the right number in each group of three to send through the multiplying machine to give the answer 91. Write one number on each dotted line.

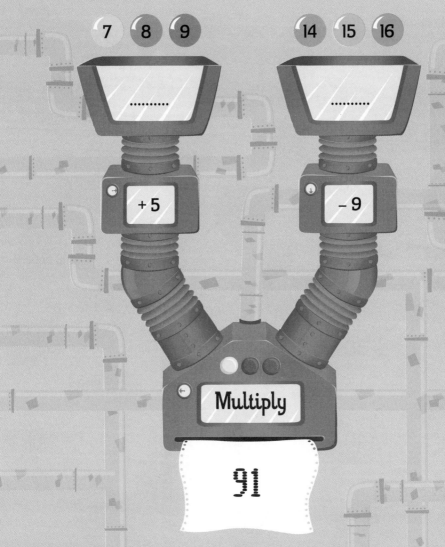

Shape sequences

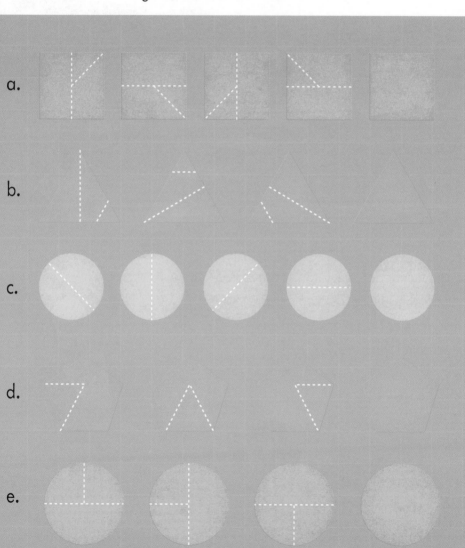

128

Draw the correct lines into the blank shapes at the end of each sequence to show the line arrangement that comes next.

a.

b.

c.

d.

e.

Racing cars

First, figure out the sequence to fill in the missing racing car numbers.

Blue: . . . .

Green: . . . .

Red: . . . .

The number of spectators is a hundred times the sum of the car numbers that are **prime**. How many people are watching the race?

Answer: . . . .

Shipshape angles

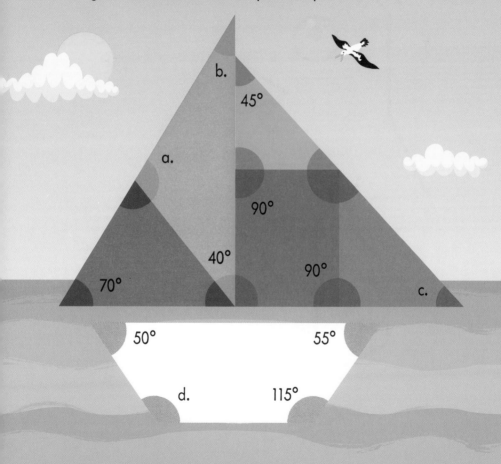

130

Figure out the size of **angles** a, b, c and d in this picture, and write them at the bottom. Use these rules to help you:

• All the angles on a straight line add up to 180°.
• All the angles inside a triangle add up to 180°.
• All the angles inside a four-sided shape add up to 360°.

b.

45°

a.

90°

40°

90°

70°

c.

50°

55°

d.

115°

a. ....   b. ....   c. ....   d. ....

Penguin reflection

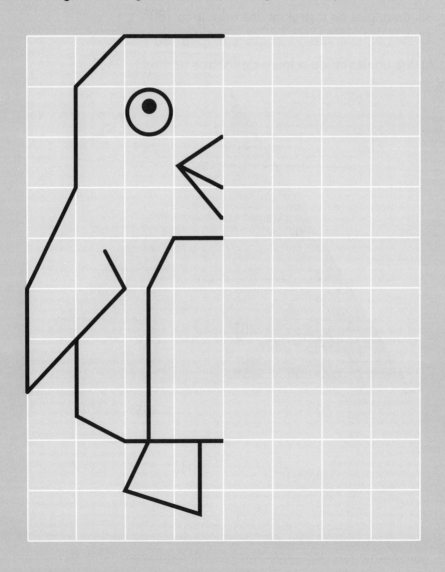

Only half of the penguin has been drawn on the grid below. Draw its **mirror image** on the right-hand side of the grid to complete the picture.

Sweet symmetry

Circle the two groups of sweet treats that can be rotated so that they match each other exactly.

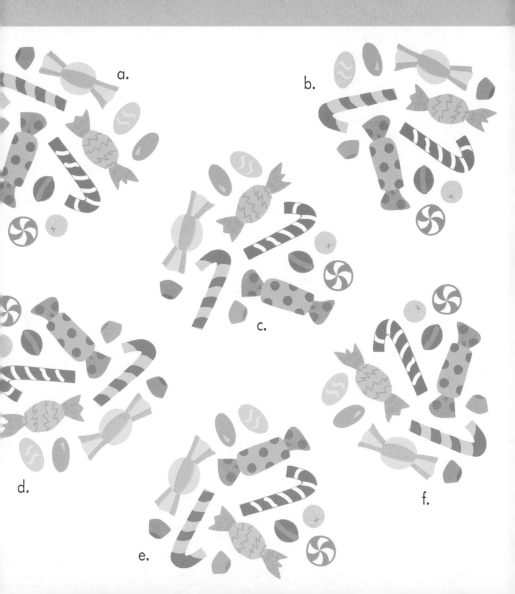

a.

b.

c.

d.

e.

f.

Marbles

Sam, Rob and Max divide a bag of marbles between themselves according to their ages. Max is the youngest and Sam is the oldest, and for every one marble that Max gets, Rob gets two and Sam gets three. Count the marbles, then write on the bags how many each boy gets.

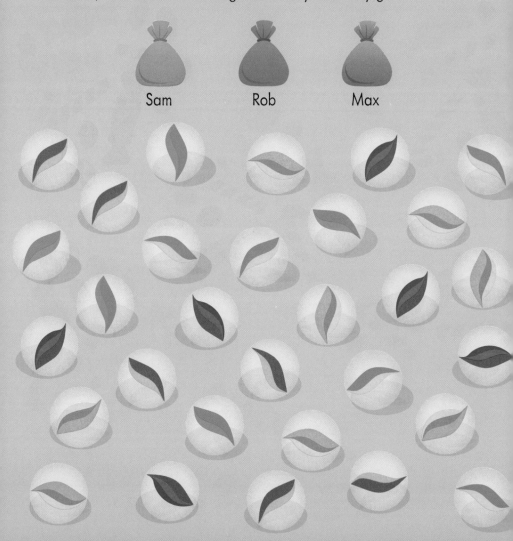

Sam   Rob   Max

Shape splitting

Shapes 1 to 4 can each be made by using a different one of these white pieces six times. Can you find out which piece makes up which shape? Hint: focus on the edges of the shape. A piece might not fit inside the shape's edge without leaving squares that can't be filled.

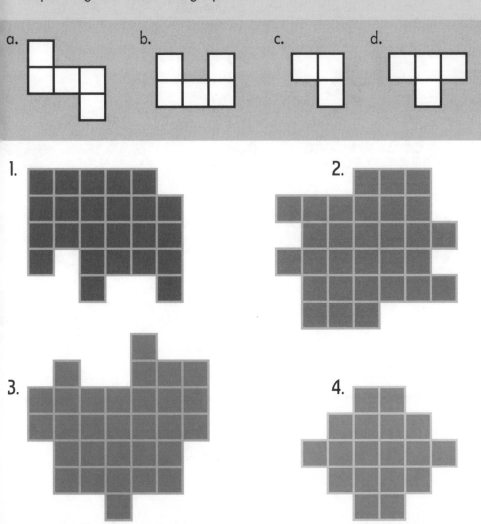

a.

b.

c.

d.

1.

2.

3.

4.

Each type of sea creature in this scene represents a different number from six to nine. All the blue fish and all the starfish together equal 72, and all the striped fish and all the jellyfish together also equal 72. Write the correct number below each creature at the bottom.

Answers:
. . . .

Sudoku

The grid is made up of nine blocks, each containing nine squares. Fill in the blank squares so that each block, row and column contains all the numbers 1 to 9.

	2	6		4				1
1				5		8		
3				2		4	6	9
				9	2			5
	6			7			3	
7			3	6				
5	8	9		1				7
		1		8				2
4				3		1	8	

Sorting snowmen

Draw three overlapping circles to group these snowmen into the three categories on the sign at the bottom. Some belong in more than one category, so make your circles overlap in the correct places so that each snowman is included in every category he falls into.

Circle 1: has a round body.
Circle 2: has a carrot nose.
Circle 3: wearing a red scarf.

Starting at the runway, divide along each plane's trail to find the number in the next cloud. The plane whose trail ends with the highest number will reach its destination first – circle it.

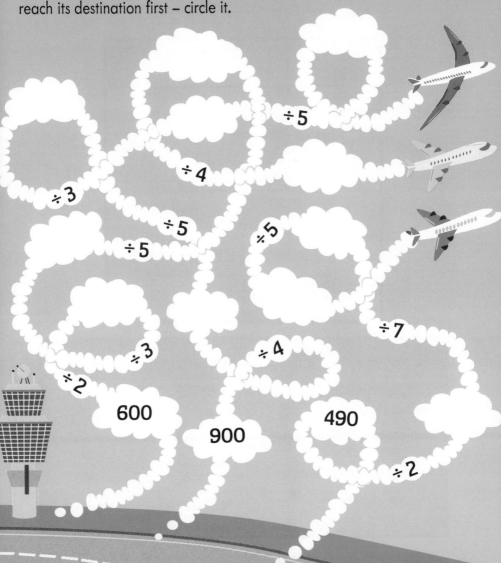

Cross-number

Use the clues at the bottom to put the correct numbers into the grid.

	1		2		
					3
4			5		
6					
			7		

Across →

1. The number of seconds in two hours and two minutes

5. The number of corners on 101 cubes

6. 16,167 minus 8,627

7. Eighty-one times five

Down ↓

1. 23 + 12 + 37

2. The number of legs in a flock of 52,101 sheep

3. The number of legs on 111 spiders

4. Eight thousand three hundred divided by four

Patchwork squares

Draw lines to divide the grid into six areas. Each area must contain the same number of squares as buttons. One area has been done for you.

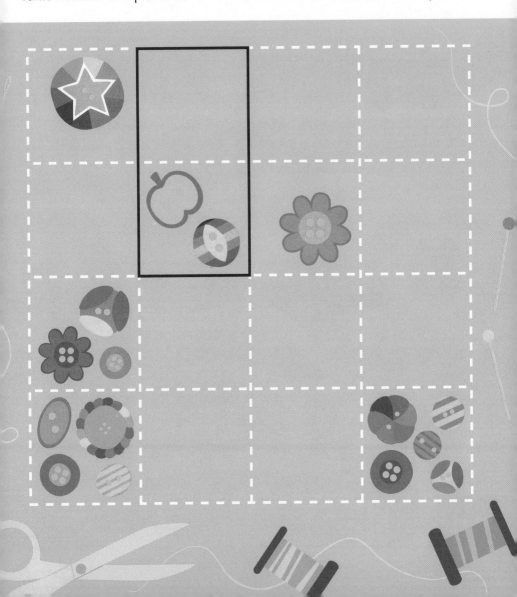

Bus route

The red bus is on its way to the next bus stop. Draw the route it will take if the driver only steers along the roads with numbers in the 9x table or the 11x table.

Honeycomb

Bertie bee can only cross the honeycomb one cell at a time. Draw the shortest route he can take to reach his friend, only crossing the cells that contain numbers that can be divided by three.

Bertie

Start

| 46 | 83 | 19 | 51 | 18 |

| 74 | 42 | 96 | 87 | 112 | 93 |

| 12 | 90 | 45 | 37 | 21 | 52 | 18 | 37 |

| 64 | 66 | 82 | 48 | 24 | 100 | 75 | 81 |

| 15 | 39 | 54 | 78 | 88 | 97 | 42 |

| 35 | 49 | 72 | 39 | 12 | 120 | 144 | 26 |

| 19 | 58 | 6 | 99 | 44 | 57 | 74 |

| 8 | 21 | 90 | 41 | 3 | 52 | Finish |

| 14 | 9 | 36 | 37 | 15 |

How many diamond shapes can you find hidden in this pattern?

A diamond shape looks like this:

Answer: . . . .

Wild West

These men live in the Wild West. The sheriff is the bravest, the mayor is the richest and the outlaw is the most wanted. Complete the calculations, then circle the man who's a bounty hunter.

Bravery: 50÷2
Wealth: 7x7
Most wanted: 84-63

Bravery: 10x6
Wealth: 99÷9
Most wanted: 25+8

Bravery: 5+23
Wealth: 12x5
Most wanted: 200÷10

Bravery: 82-23
Wealth: 7+10
Most wanted: 5x8

These robots process numbers, changing the number on the left cog into a new number, which is shown on the right cog. For each robot, fill in the blanks so that the calculations are correct.

Cake baking

Who took the longest time to bake and finish decorating their cake?
Which baker finished making their cake in the shortest time?

Started   **Finished**

Izzy

Ryan

Elsa

James

Longest time: ....   Shortest time: ....

Cross fit

Can you fit all six shapes below inside the cross without any overlapping or going outside the lines? Draw the shapes, or cut them out, to show how you would arrange them inside the cross. (You may need to rotate some of them.

Egg and spoon race

Five children competed in an egg and spoon race. Add up each racer's time in seconds, adding 12 seconds for a drop. Circle the child who reached the finish line first.

(!) = a drop

Fruit and vegetables

You need all of the items on the shopping list at the bottom. Count up the fruit and vegetables on this market stall, then draw a cross next to the items that you won't have enough of.

Shopping List		
5 apples	8 bananas	
1 pineapple	4 bunches of grapes	
12 pears	6 carrots	
2 pumpkins	3 red peppers	

Hook a duck

Which ducks have the highest average score: red or blue? Add up the total of the blue numbers and divide it by the number of blue ducks. Then do the same with the red numbers and red ducks to find out which gives the higher answer.

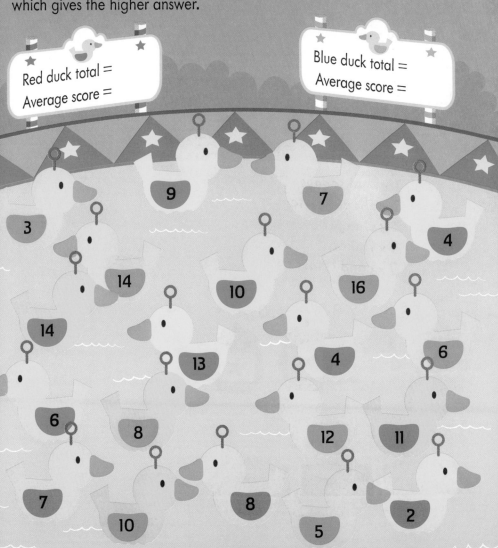

Red duck total =
Average score =

Blue duck total =
Average score =

Sundae special

The orders for the last three sundaes of the day have come in. Once they've been made, how much of each ingredient will you have left for your own sundae? Draw it in the empty glass, using everything that's left.

1 x strawberry scoop
1 x mint scoop
2 x chocolate scoops
2 x flakes
2 x wafers
5 x candy stars

3 x strawberry scoops
4 x cherries
2 x wafers
10 x candy stars

2 x mint scoops
2 x chocolate scoops
1 x cherry
4 x flakes
7 x candy stars

Eagle escape

The meerkat lookouts have spotted an eagle flying their way. If the same number of meerkats scurry down each hole, and three are left out in the open when the eagle arrives, how many meerkats are hiding down each one? Write your answer on the hole at the bottom.

Hedgehog hurry

Guide Hetty the hedgehog through the maze to Harry. What is the sum of the numbers she goes through on her way?

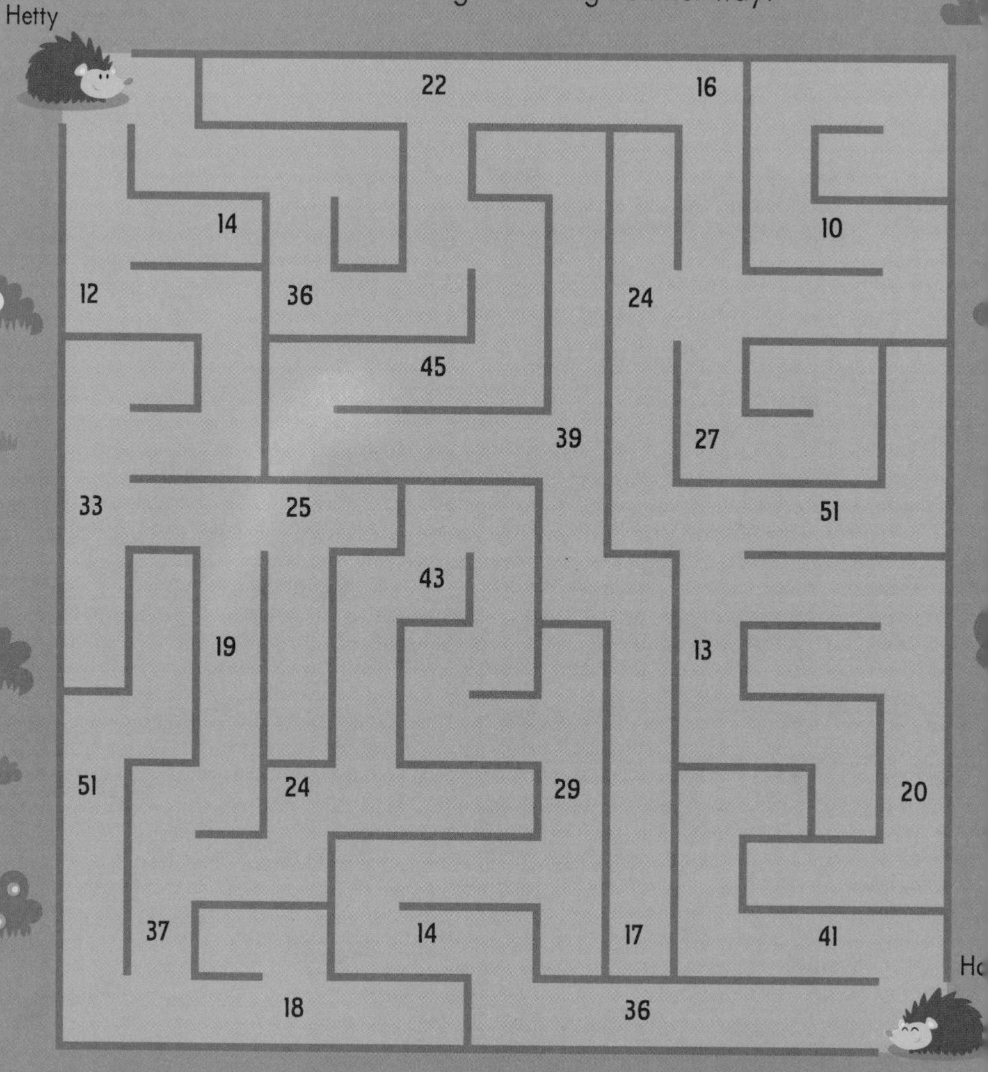

Hetty

22   16

14   10

12   36   24

45

39   27

33   25   51

43

19   13

51   24   29   20

37   14   17   41

18   36

Ha

Answer: . . . .

Balancing act

The first two sets of scales below are balanced, but the bottom set is not. Which weight should you add on the right-hand side to make the third set balance? Draw your answer on the scales.

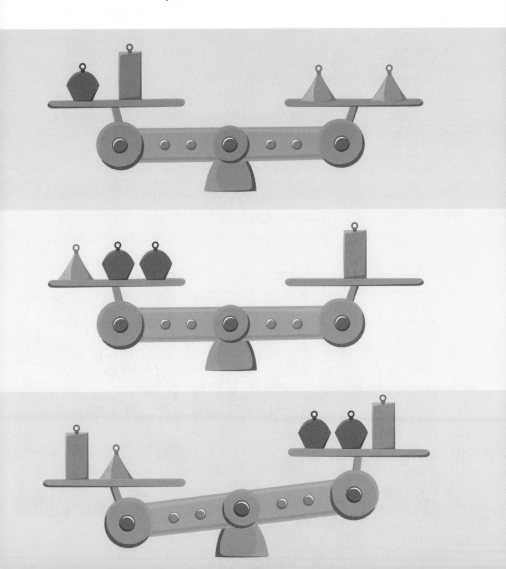

Secret mission

A microchip containing top secret data is hidden in the city park, and you're on a mission to retrieve it. Use the instructions below to find the **coordinates** for the correct square on the map at the bottom.

On the map, fill in:

• all the squares with coordinates that add up to an odd number.

• all the squares that give an answer of less than 12 when you multiply their coordinates.

• all the squares that give an answer of 18 or more when you multiply their coordinates.

The remaining square that is not touching any other unfilled square is where the microchip is buried. Put an X in that square on the map.

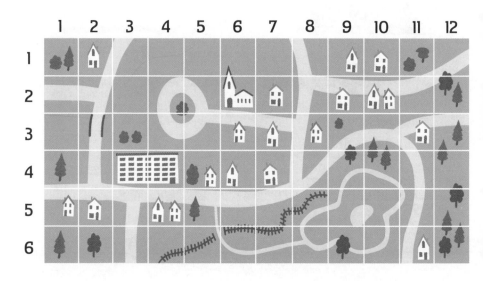

On the farm

Join all the dots in the order of the 3x table to reveal what's making all the noise in the farmyard this morning.

Mirror writing

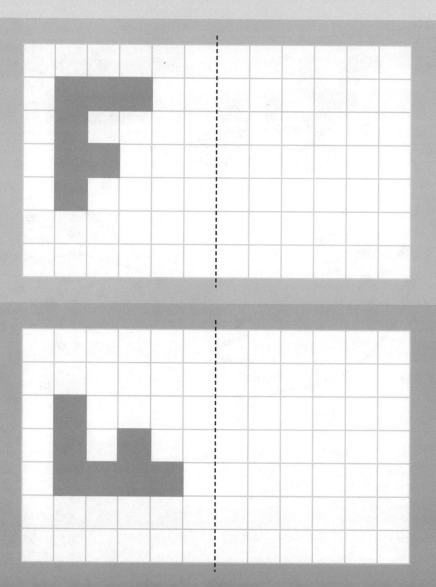

The dotted black lines on the grids below are mirrors. Draw the **mirror image** of each F-shape in the correct place on the other half of its grid.

Find eighteen

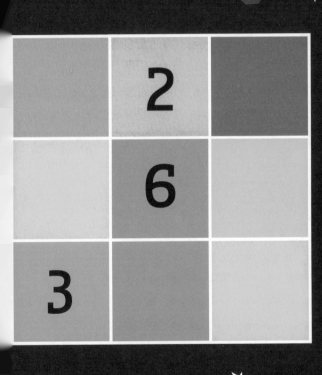

mbers 2 to 10 into the grid below, so that the numbers
column and diagonal line of three add up to 18.
numbers have already been filled in for you.

	2	
	6	
3		

The Round Table

King Arthur had a round table, so that his knights wouldn't argue over who was sitting in the most important places. Use the clues below to fill in the missing names on the table. (Remember, there are 360 degrees in a circle.)

1. Sir Tristram sat at 300 degrees from Sir Galahad.

2. Sir Gawain sat at 90 degrees from Sir Gareth.

3. Sir Bedivere sat at 60 degrees from Sir Gareth.

4. Sir Percival and Sir Ector sat at 180 degrees from each other.

5. Sir Kay sat at 240 degrees from the king.

6. Sir Ector sat at 120 degrees from Sir Kay.

Race to the Lost Isles

Fill in the missing numbers on each explorer's ship, so that all three masts add up to the same total. The ship whose top three sails add up to the highest number will be the first to reach the Lost Isles. Which will it be?

Prime predator

The prime predator gobbles up any number that's **prime**. Circle the five numbers that he won't eat.

37   2   19

29   53   27   47   31

65   17

13   41

7   23

11

3   59

18   21

43   5   33

All of these trains take 37 minutes to reach your destination, but you need to arrive between 12:05 and 12:35. Write down the arrival time for each train, then draw an X on the train you need to catch.

DEPART	11:59
ARRIVE	....

DEPART	11:16
ARRIVE	....

DEPART	11:27
ARRIVE	....

DEPART	11:48
ARRIVE	....

Balancing act

163

The first two sets of scales below are balanced, but the bottom set is not. Which weight should you add on the right-hand side to make the third set balance? Draw your answer on the scales.

Knights' shields

Solve the calculations to find out which paint to use for each section of the shields below – each answer is the number on the correct can of paint. Then, draw lines to match each knight to his shiny new shield.

$144 \div 12$

$42 - 37$

$71 - 59$

$80 \div 16$

$250 \div 50$

$56 \div 7$

$40 \div 5$

2×4

$20 - 15$

$36 - 29$

$49 \div 7$

$100 \div 20$

$84 \div 12$

7

5

12

8

Secret cipher

Agent 003.6 is trying to decode a top secret message from his spymaster. Can you use the **percentages** on the screen below to write the correct letter under each number and help him find out what it says?

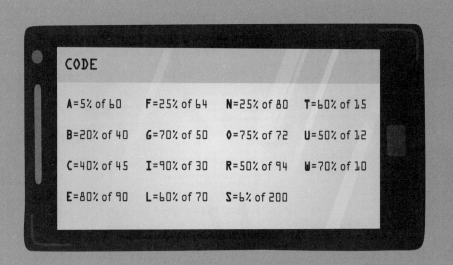

CODE

A=5% of 60   F=25% of 64   N=25% of 80   T=60% of 15

B=20% of 40   G=70% of 50   O=75% of 72   U=50% of 12

C=40% of 45   I=90% of 30   R=50% of 94   W=70% of 10

E=80% of 90   L=60% of 70   S=6% of 200

MESSAGE:

3 | 42 | 42   3 | 35 | 72 | 20 | 9 | 12   47 | 72 | 9 | 6 | 47 | 20

9 | 54   8 | 3 | 12 | 72   16 | 54 | 47   20 | 72 | 7

27 | 20 | 12 | 9 | 47 | 6 | 18 | 9 | 27 | 54 | 20 | 12

Number search

The answers to the calculations at the bottom of the page are hidden in the grid below. They may be written in any direction. When you find each one, draw around it, as shown on the right.

7	4	5	2	3	7	1	9
2	2	0	4	7	9	0	7
8	8	7	4	0	3	8	5
1	7	3	5	4	9	7	1
3	9	1	4	6	9	5	4
0	9	4	5	5	1	9	4
8	3	1	1	4	7	0	9
4	7	9	7	0	3	1	2

120 − 6 = ?	12 × 9 = ?	108 ÷ 9 = ?
69 ÷ 3 = ?	88 ÷ 4 = ?	5 × 7 = ?
48 + 13 = ?	8 + 76 = ?	12 × 12 = ?

Whose room?

167

Four friends – Tom, Natalie, Faye and Pete – have all drawn floorplans of their bedrooms, but which is which? Use the clues below to find out, then write each friend's name inside the plan they've drawn.

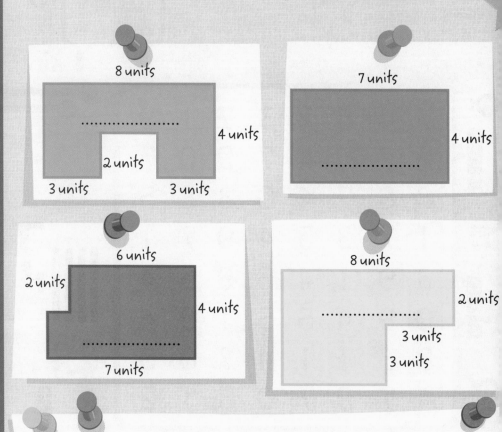

8 units

4 units

2 units

3 units   3 units

7 units

4 units

6 units

2 units

4 units

7 units

8 units

2 units

3 units

3 units

- The number of units in the **perimeter** of Tom's room is the same as the number of square units in the **area** of his room.

- The **area** of Natalie's room is the same number of square units as the number of units there are in the **perimeter** of Faye's room.

Flying saucer

Join all the purple dots in the order of the 12x table, then join all the
blue dots in the order of the 11x table to finish building this alien's
flying saucer.

Tile-hop

Bess can only step on tiles with numbers that divide by 3. Jess can only step on tiles with numbers that divide by 4. They can move to a tile that touches theirs along one side, but not one that just touches at a corner. Who will cross the floor using the fewest number of tiles?

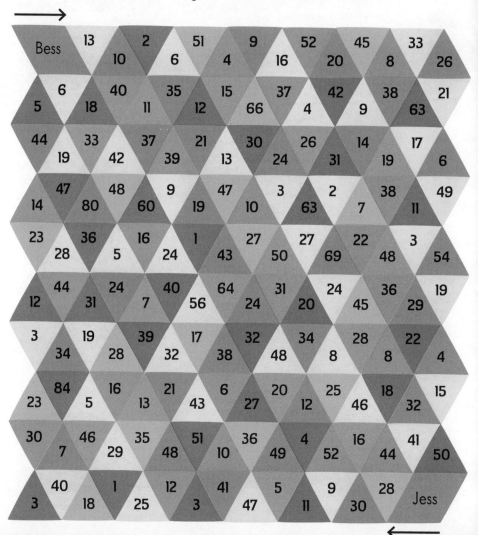

Basketball challenge

Write the missing numbers on the basketballs so that any two balls next to each other multiply together to make the number on the ball above. This player's score is the number on the top ball. Did he beat the score on the board? Fill in 'Yes' or 'No' to leave the correct answer showing.

46

Answer:
Yes / No

6

4

3

2

Alien height chart

These aliens measure their height in units called zurgs. If each alien grows ten zurgs a month until it is 60 zurgs tall, and five zurgs a month after that, who will be 85 zurgs tall in eight months' time? Measure the aliens from the tops of their heads and then circle the correct one.

100zg

90zg

80zg

70zg

60zg

50zg

40zg

30zg

20zg

10zg

Fruit puzzle

The key at the bottom of the page tells you how many pieces of each fruit make one serving. If you eat two servings a day, how many days will the fruit supply below last?

Answer: . . . .

Each of these pictures shows one serving of fruit:

Time difference

These clocks show the different times in cities all over the world. The time in Paris is ten hours behind the time in Sydney. Lisbon is nine hours behind Tokyo and five hours ahead of New York. Dubai is three hours ahead of Paris. Write each city's name under the correct clock.

Sydney

Taking the bait

These fish will only swallow the numbers that are 80% of the numbers on their bodies. Draw a circle around the fish that won't get caught.

Picture code

Each picture below stands for a different number from 1 to 4. The numbers at the edges of the grid are the sum of the numbers in each row or column. Can you figure out which picture represents which number?

Answers:

Butterfly symmetry

Only half of the butterfly has been drawn on the grid below. Draw its **mirror image** on the left-hand side of the grid to complete the picture.

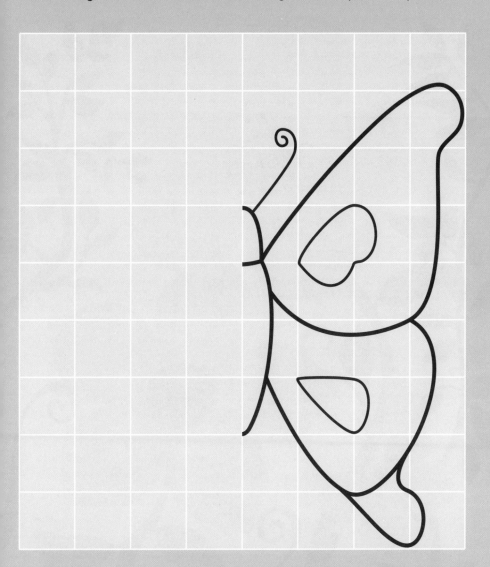

Petal pairs

Fill in the missing numbers so that both parts of each petal add up to the number in the middle of the flower.

44

3

-6

37

28

-15

64

-19

-3

-8

17

-12

Skyscraper scramble

178

Help the spy climb up to the roof of the skyscraper without being seen. He can only cross windows whose numbers can be divided by 3, but he mustn't cross a window if its number can also be divided by 5. He can't climb diagonally either.

76	55	85	15	90	65	30	9	47	31	25	70	56	65	35	60
95	18	12	42	24	81	27	36	20	40	73	11	82	10	79	26
55	3	65	10	95	50	7	31	5	38	25	45	80	43	40	47
75	57	40	72	39	63	20	90	51	66	78	48	33	54	21	69
60	87	6	36	40	96	18	81	84	55	70	25	65	90	75	3
41	20	35	70	5	65	30	95	37	10	78	72	12	93	42	6
23	80	69	66	54	33	24	52	60	75	57	40	95	45	15	80
46	15	51	70	55	30	48	21	9	63	39	40	58	19	61	28
8	49	27	71	16	29	10	83	65	30	70	32	4	45	74	13
34	10	81	35	90	20	69	60	36	18	72	35	66	77	44	86
57	50	42	5	69	12	54	75	78	25	63	6	48	39	45	70
22	95	24	51	9	30	33	21	57	55	67	53	45	66	27	3
5	64	75	20	95	14	65	30	45	62	15	55	2	60	35	🧍

Running total

Find each runner's total to see how quickly he will get around the track. The one with the lowest total will cross the finish line first. Circle the winner.

START

FINISH

1 + 6 15 = = 3

4 + 3 + 6 + 10 11 + 1

9 + 7 + 12 + 16 5 + 8

3 + 4 + 9 13 5 + 3 + 5

8 + 3 + 1 + 8 + 3 6 + 5 + 1

7 + 17 + 9 + 11 + 13

12 + 2 + 16

2 1 3

Lake routes

Three families leave their homes at the same time and drive to the lake, taking different routes. Circle the family who will reach the lake first if...

...the Hall family drives up and down one hill every ten minutes, but has to go back home for their sandwiches, which adds 25 minutes to their time.

...the Jones family drives up and down one hill every 11 minutes, but spends ten minutes fixing an engine problem.

...the Collins family drives up and down one hill every 12 minutes, and drives to the lake without stopping.

The dotted black lines on the grids below are mirrors. Draw the **mirror image** of each triangle in the correct place on the other half of its grid.

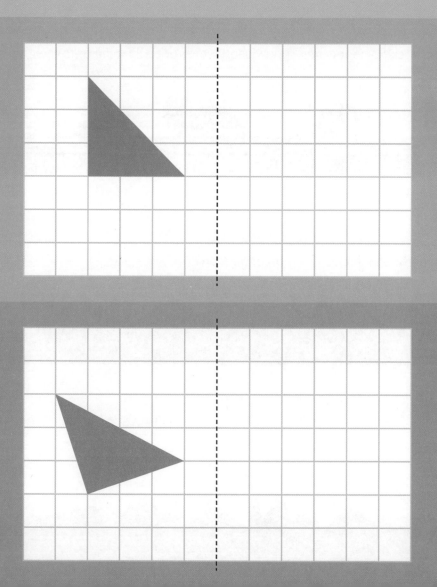

Germ twins

Circle the two groups of germs that can be rotated so that they match each other exactly.

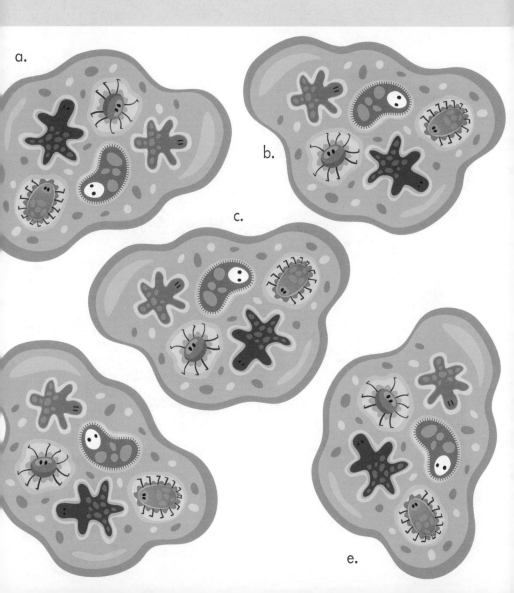

a.

b.

c.

e.

Island bus

43 passengers were on the island bus when it left the ferry. The stops show how many people got on and off at each one, but one number is missing. If 17 passengers arrived at Cove House, how many people got on at Dolphin Park?

On: 11
Off: 9

On: 4
Off: 30

Cove House

On: 2
Off: 7

On: 6
Off: 11

Start

On: ....
Off: 12

Dolphin Park

On: 21
Off: 16

Space for calculations

Answers

1 Racetrack
Yes, his time is 2 minutes and 29 seconds

2 Farm fours

2	1	4⁷	3
3	4⁶	1	2
4	2	3	1⁵
1⁶	3	2	4

3 Number cruncher

39 57 63 27

4 Pirate voyage

5 Across the ice

6 Frog friends

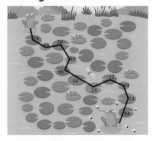

7 Chickens and eggs
Draw six eggs.

8 Number search

43+16+37 = 96   67+55+14 = 136   23×11 = 253
84÷6 = 14   174-117 = 57   95÷5 = 19
90×4 = 360   78÷3 = 26   108-31 = 77

9 Toy store
2 tokens left

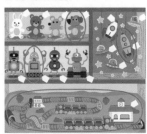

10 Delivering letters
0.5 x 10 = House 5

$\frac{2}{7}$ of 28 = House 8

10% of 90 = House 9

$\frac{1}{9}$ of 63 = House 7

84 ÷ 21 = House 4

42.2 – 36.2 = House 6

11 Destination data

Number of people	
Ski trip:	12
City break:	18
Cruise:	9
Beach break:	24
Safari:	9

Answers

12 Seaside scene
There are 8 crabs,
9 pieces of seaweed,
12 flags and 5 starfish.
Answer: 11

13 Kayak course

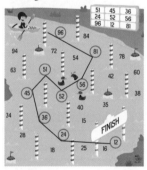

14 Gymnastics

	Under 12	Under 16	Total
America	4	10	14
Russia	8	9	17
China	9	13	22
Britain	1	4	5
Total	22	36	58

15 Planet problems

16 Dice spots

17 Burger bar
8 cheeseburgers

CHEESEBURGER
RECIPE
(per serving)
12 burger buns   20÷2=10 lettuce leaves
15 burgers   16 rings of onion
24÷3=8 slices of tomato 20 slices of cheese

2 x 10 = 20   2 x 6 = 12   3 x 5 = 15

2 x 8 = 16   4 x 6 = 24   1 x 20 = 20

18 Find fifteen

8	3	4
1	5	9
6	7	2

19 Crazy golf
Charlie's score is 31.
(2+3+4+6+7+5+4=31)
The course record is 30,
so he didn't beat it.

20 Robot workers

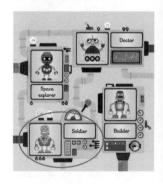

21 Which cube?
B

Answers

22 Hidden picture

23 Cat calculation
210
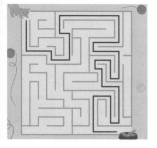

24 Building a nest
Yes

25 In the jungle

26 Fish patterns
Stripes: 10   Spots: 5
Swirls: 4   Zigzags: 3
3 fish are left plain.

27 Butterfly farm
Striped: 40%
Spotted: 25%
Hairy: 75%

28 Domino sequences
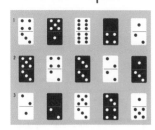

29 Coconut shy

5 + 6 + 2   3 + 9 + 13   7 + 10 + 11

30 Starfish split
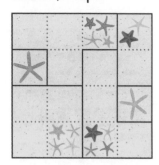

31 Birds on branches
10 birds are left:
Orange: 2
Blue: 3
Yellow: 1
Other: 4

32 Canyon crossing

Answers

33 Locomotive loads

The red train

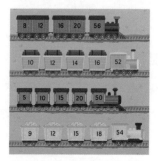

34 Top dogs

Dog's name	Discipline	Tricks	Appearance	Total
Fido	8	5	7	20
Benji	6	10	8	24
Rusty	10	9	6	25

35 Fastest route

36 Darts scores

a. $(1+2+3) = 6$

b. $(18+22+26) = 66$

c. 4 (1, 2 and 7; 1, 3 and 6; 1, 4 and 5; 2, 3 and 5)

37 Bridge crossing

Unsafe planks:

$42 \div 7 = 6$, not 7

$13 + 29 = 42$, not 44

$335 - 177 = 158$, not 156

$14 \times 5 = 70$, not 72

38 Maze meeting

3 minutes (180 seconds)

39 On the seabed

40 Taking taxis

No, there will be one person left over. (There are 19 people, but only 18 spaces available.)

41 Cross-number

2	3	5	7		
	6			4	5
	0				7
1	0	6	9	8	3
6			0		9
	7	0	8		

42 Balancing act

Answers

43 Token total
40

44 House of horrors
8 Horrors

45 Nectar numbers

46 Cross sum

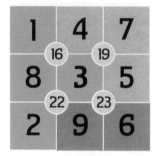

47 Seating arrangements
Ages: 33, 35, 7, 7
Seats: 19, 20, 21, 22

48 Cake decorating
Each cake should have
8 sprinkles, 2 flakes, 3
marshmallows, 1 cherry
and 1 ribbon.

49 Circles and squares

1	4	7
8	3	5
2	9	6

16, 19, 22, 23

50 Bubble burst

51 Coconut climb

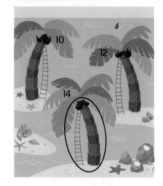

52 Castle copy

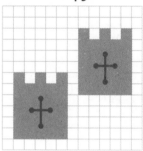

53 In the park

Number of people	
Have a picnic:	10
Use the swings:	10
Walk the dog:	15
Fly a kite:	5
Play sports:	20

Answers

54 Birthday surprise

55 Bingo buddies

56 Triangle count
37

57 Fruit filling

Amount to be packed	Pallets (1,000 items each)	Crates (100 items each)	Boxes (10 items each)	Single items left unpacked
4,187 pineapples	4	1	8	7
58,713 apples	58	7	1	3
74,607 oranges	74	6	0	7
406,079 bananas	406	0	7	9
2,309,218 strawberries	2309	2	1	8

58 Airport maze

59 Crossing the lake
7 trips

60 Flower show

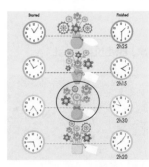

61 Excess baggage
The bag that weighs
11 units

62 Shape fitting

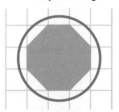

63 Washing lines

64 Pool planner

	Morning	Afternoon	Total
2 – 4 years old	7	1	8
4 – 6 years old	11	2	13
6 – 8 years old	12	9	21
8 – 10 years old	6	26	32
Total	36	38	74

65 Traffic times
$6 \times 5 \times 4 \times 2 = 240$ Slowest
$3 \times 4 \times 5 \times 3 = 180$
$2 \times 3 \times 4 \times 7 = 168$
$3 \times 2 \times 7 \times 3 = 126$ Fastest
$4 \times 2 \times 3 \times 8 = 192$

Answers

66 Ice skaters
Hats: 3
Scarves: 3
Ear muffs: 4
2 skaters are left.

67 Pyramid puzzle

68 Airport luggage
Yes, there are 42 items of luggage in total, which is the same amount that the luggage carts can hold.

69 Tangram square

70 Hidden picture

71 Under the sea
Fish: 12
Jellyfish: 6
Crab: 54

72 Sequence search
40, 47, 54, 61, 68
41, 47, 53, 59, 65
56, 60, 64, 68, 72
7, 10, 13, 16, 19
60, 62, 64, 66, 68

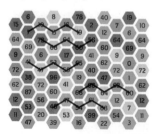

73 Number mix
Yellow potion 5 and red potion 2

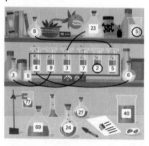

74 Driving home

75 Pirate emporium
12 pieces:

2 parrots = 56
1 globe = 24
12 goblets = 48
1 hat = 8
5 hooks = 16
15 bottles = 36

Total = 188

200 − 188 = 12

Answers

76 Minigolf
Sara scored lowest
with 56.
Jamie: 57
Zoe: 58

77 Duck directions
136

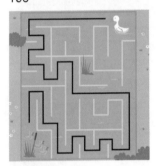

78 Petal count
Samir will have the
biggest bouquet.

79 Six sudoku

4	2	3	5	1	6
5	6	1	3	2	4
1	5	4	2	6	3
2	3	6	4	5	1
3	1	2	6	4	5
6	4	5	1	3	2

80 Space chart

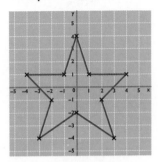

81 Bees and hives
There are 40 bees.
25 live in the big hive,
15 live in the small hive.

82 Toolbox trouble
There are 7 screwdrivers
6 hammers, 16 bolts and
7 wrenches.
The missing tool is a
screwdriver.

83 Cross sum

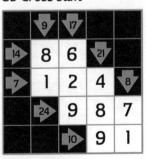

84 Strength test
177 − 112 = 65
The middle of 65 is 33 (32
on either side), so Sophie's
score was 144.

85 Which cube?
C

86 Racing roller coaster

87 Hungry robot

Answers

88 Car categories
The green car belongs to the farmer.
Yellow car: Banker's
Red car: Stunt driver's
Blue car: Movie star's

89 Ski race
Red: 145 seconds
Blue: 144 seconds

90 Planet puzzle

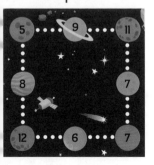

91 Compass points

The needle swings 45° clockwise.	NE
Then, it swings 270° in the opposite direction.	SE
Lastly, it swings 135° clockwise.	W

92 Roman emperors
1. Nero
2. Gaius
3. AD 79
4. 78

93 Owl symmetry

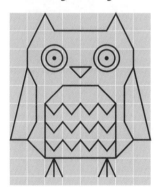

94 Picture code

1   3   2   4

95 Plane passengers
12 trips

96 Alien escape
5 aliens

97 Apple picking

98 Pipes puzzle

Answers

99 Beach fours

⁷4	1	3	2
3	⁶2	4	1
1	3	2	4
⁶2	4	1	3

100 Sudoku

6	8	5	1	3	7	2	9	4
7	4	3	9	2	6	5	8	1
2	1	9	5	8	4	6	3	7
5	3	8	7	9	1	4	6	2
4	9	2	6	5	3	7	1	8
1	7	6	2	4	8	3	5	9
3	2	7	8	6	9	1	4	5
9	6	1	4	7	5	8	2	3
8	5	4	3	1	2	9	7	6

101 Space race

102 Rocket re-size

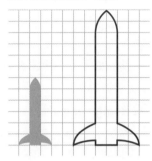

103 Hidden hieroglyphs

104 Picture code

3   1   4   2

105 Treasure chests

106 Sailing fours

⁷4	2	⁴1	3
3	4	2	1
³2	1	3	⁶4
1	3	4	2

107 Folding shapes

108 Town planning

Answers

109 Safe cracker

Turn the dial 60% clockwise.	40
Then, turn the dial 90% in the opposite direction.	30
Then, turn the dial 25% clockwise.	5
Lastly, turn the dial 85% in the opposite direction.	90

110 Monster mirror

111 Pharaoh timeline

1. Ramesses II
2. Ramesses I
3. 26 years
4. 18

112 Turning tools

a and d

(Mistakes circled in red)

113 Butterfly wings

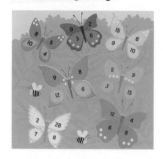

114 Out in space

115 Missing angles

a. 45°
b. 55°
c. 35°
d. 125°

116 Germ colony

Thursday: 76 germs
Wednesday: 38 germs
On Tuesday there were
19 germs.

117 Street scene

1) $16 - 4 = 4 + 6$ (False)
2) $2 + 4 + 4 = 16 - 6$ (True)
3) $16 \div 4 = 2 \times 2$ (True)
4) $4 + 4 = 16 \div 2$ (True)
5) $4 + 4 = 16 \times 2$ (False)

118 Hidden picture

119 Chore chart

Lyla: 11 stickers
Sam: 10 stickers

120 Gone fishing

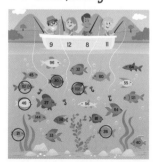

Answers

121 Weight lifters

122 Circles and squares

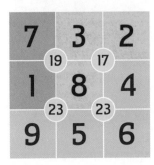

123 Which bus?

Simon: 11:50
Charlotte: 10:00

124 Cattle round-up

9 minutes and
45 seconds

125 Cube in a cube

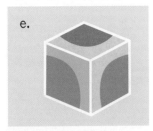

e.

126 Snails and leaves

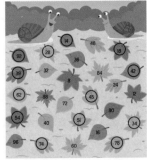

127 Multiplying machine

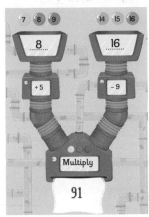

128 Shape sequences

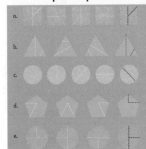

129 Racing cars

Blue: 19
Green: 23
Red: 29
7,100 spectators

130 Shipshape angles

a. 120°
b. 20°
c. 45°
d. 140°

131 Penguin reflection

Answers

132 Sweet symmetry

d and f

(Mistakes circled in red)

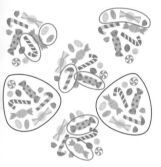

133 Marbles

Sam: 15
Rob: 10
Max: 5

134 Shape splitting

a. 3
b. 2
c. 4
d. 1

135 Undersea sums

7   8   6   9

136 Sudoku

9	2	6	8	4	3	7	5	1
1	4	7	6	5	9	8	2	3
3	5	8	1	2	7	4	6	9
8	1	3	4	9	2	6	7	5
2	6	4	5	7	1	9	3	8
7	9	5	3	6	8	2	1	4
5	8	9	2	1	6	3	4	7
6	3	1	7	8	4	5	9	2
4	7	2	9	3	5	1	8	6

137 Sorting snowmen

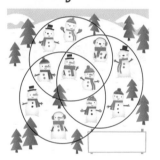

138 Destination division

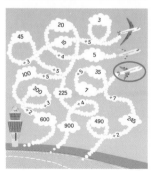

139 Cross-number

	7	3	2	0	
	2		0		8
2		8	0	8
0			4		8
7	5	4	0	
5			4	0	5

140 Patchwork squares

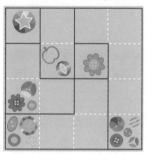

141 Bus route

Answers

142 Honeycomb

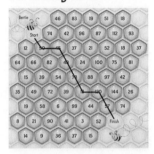

143 Diamond count

38

144 Wild West

Bounty hunter   Sheriff   Mayor   Outlaw

145 Number robots

146 Cake baking

Izzy: 3h, 20 (Longest time)
Ryan: 2h, 35
Elsa: 3h, 10
James: 2h, 20 (Shortest time)

147 Cross fit

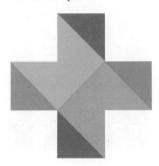

148 Egg and spoon race

40   44   42   (39)   41

149 Fruit and vegetables

There are only five carrots on the stall, and only 11 pears.

150 Hook a duck

Red duck total = 88
Red duck average = 8

Blue duck total = 81
Blue duck average = 9

151 Sundae special

1 strawberry scoop
1 chocolate scoop
2 mint scoops
1 wafer
1 cherry
2 flakes
8 candy stars

152 Eagle escape

Five meerkats are hiding down each hole.

153 Hedgehog hurry

210

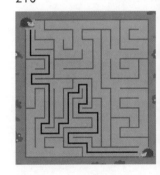

154 Balancing act

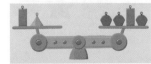

Answers

155 Secret mission

(8, 2)

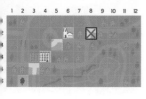

156 On the farm

157 Mirror writing

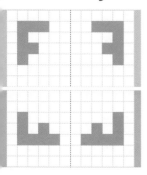

158 Find eighteen

7	2	9
8	6	4
3	10	5

159 The Round Table

160 Race to the Lost Isles

161 Prime predator

162 Catch the train

163 Balancing act

Answers

164 Knights' shields

165 Secret cipher

All agents return to base
for new instructions

166 Number search

167 Whose room?

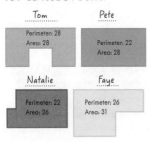

168 Flying saucer

169 Tile-hop

Bess: 24 tiles
Jess: 22 tiles
Jess won

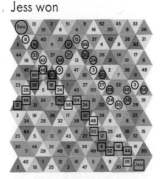

170 Basketball challenge

He scored 48, so he beat
the score on the board.

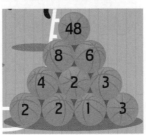

171 Alien height chart

172 Fruit puzzle

12 days

173 Time difference

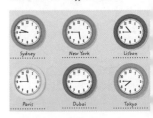

174 Taking the bait

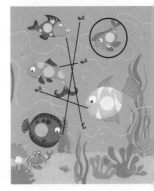

Answers

175 Picture code

4   1   2   3

176 Butterfly symmetry

177 Petal pairs

178 Skyscraper scramble

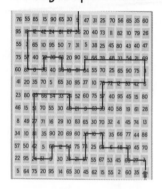

179 Running total

180 Lake routes

The Jones family will get to the lake first.
Hall family: 55 minutes
Jones family: 54 minutes
Collins family: 60 minutes

181 Triangle reflections

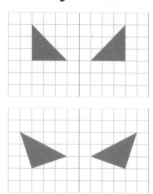

182 Germ twins

c and e
(Mistakes circled in red)

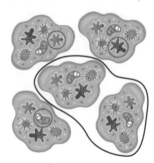

183 Island bus

15 people got on at Dolphin Park.

Help sheet

You can use the information on the next two pages to help you solve some of the puzzles in this pad.

Lines of symmetry:
A line of symmetry is a line you can draw through a shape to divide it into two matching halves.

Examples:

0 lines of symmetry   1 line of symmetry   3 lines of symmetry   4 lines of symmetry

Fractions:
Fractions are parts of a whole, and are written like this: 1/4. The second number is how many parts of that size make up a whole. The first number shows how many of those parts you're referring to.

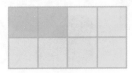

So, 1/4 is one of four equal parts that make up the whole. 1/4 of eight is two (in darker blue). 3/4 of eight is six (in lighter blue).

Decimals:
A decimal is another way of writing a fraction. A half is written as 0.5 (because 0.5 is half of 1), and a quarter is written as 0.25. Three quarters is 0.75.

Percentages:
A percentage (%) is a fraction of 100. So, half of something is 50%, because 50 is half of 100

Examples:
• To find 20% of 150, divide 150 by 10 to find 10%. This gives you 15. For 20%, multiply your answer by 2. So, 20% of 150 is 30.

• To find out what percentage 8 is of 32, divide 32 by 8, which equals 4. Then find out what goes into 100 four times to get the percentage 100÷4=25, so 8 is 25% of 32.

Number lines and negative numbers:
A number line shows numbers in order.

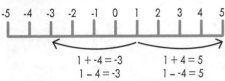

$$1 + -4 = -3 \qquad 1 + 4 = 5$$
$$1 - 4 = -3 \qquad 1 - -4 = 5$$

Negative numbers are numbers below zero. -1 is one less than zero. To add or subtract a negative number, move the opposite way on the number line than if you were adding or subtracting a positive number.

Prime numbers:
A prime number can only be divided by itself and 1 (1 is not a prime number). 2 is the only even prime number. 3, 5 and 7 are all prime, but 9 is not because it can also be divided by